Build Your Own Shortwave Antennas

Second Edition

Andrew Yoder

TAB Books

Division of McGraw-Hill, Inc.

New York   San Francisco   Washington, D.C.   Auckland   Bogotá
Caracas   Lisbon   London   Madrid   Mexico City   Milan
Montreal   New Delhi   San Juan   Singapore
Sydney   Tokyo   Toronto

© 1994 by **TAB Books**.
Published by TAB Books, a division of McGraw-Hill, Inc.

pbk 1 2 3 4 5 6 7 8 9 DOH/DOH 9 9 8 7 6 5 4

Library of Congress Cataloging-in-Publication Data
Yoder, Andrew R.
   Build your own shortwave antennas / by Andrew Yoder. — 2nd ed.
     p.   cm.
   Includes index.
   ISBN 0-07-076534-0 (pbk.)
   1. Shortwave radio—Antennas—Amateurs' manuals.   I. Title.
TK9956.Y64 1994
621.384'151—dc20   94-10829
                                                          CIP

Acquisitions editor: Roland S. Phelps
Editorial team: John T. Arthur, Book Editor
               Susan W. Kagey, Managing Editor
               Joanne Slike, Executive Editor
               Joann Woy, Indexer
Production team: Katherine G. Brown, Director
               Susan E. Hansford, Coding
               Ollie Harmon, Coding
               Patsy D. Harne, Desktop Operator
               Joan Wieland, Proofreading
               Toya Warner, Computer Illustrator
               Stephanie Myers, Computer Illustrator
Design team: Jaclyn J. Boone, Designer
               Brian Allison, Associate Designer
Cover design: Cindy Staub, Littlestown, Pa.   0765340
Cover copy writer: Michael Crowner   EL1

Most of this book was written during illnesses: while I had the flu, my wife had sinus infections, and my son had chicken pox. Here's to nagging illnesses. And here's especially to those who are nice enough to care for sick people.

Contents

Acknowledgments

When working on this book, I relied upon help (in one form or another) from many people. Thanks to Roland S. Phelps, Walt Williamson, Bill Taylor, Joe Carr, Harry Helms, Anita McCormick, Bob Ostrander, Stacey Spurlock, John Baker, my parents and in-laws, John T. Arthur, Joanne Slike, Kriss Lively-Helman, and Susan Kagey. Thanks also to the art, typesetting, and layout departments at TAB Books for the fine job. Thanks especially to Yvonne for helping to keep me on target and not letting me fall off any roofs or out of any trees over the past few years!

Introduction

Although dozens of antenna books have been published over the past 60 years, nearly all have targeted professional radio technicians (in the commercial or military sectors) or amateur radio operators. The few antenna books that have been intended for shortwave listeners were aimed at people who invested a great amount of money in their equipment and who planned that shortwave would play a significant role in their lives.

The second edition of *Build Your Own Shortwave Antennas* isn't a typical antenna book. Chapter 1, which covers beginner and makeshift antennas, is targeted at the many people who have recently purchased shortwave radios and who want to improve their reception. Just as many people want to enjoy watching movies on their VCRs without being video technicians, many people want to enjoy worldwide news, music, interviews, radio plays, and information without making shortwave their hobby. In addition to featuring simple antennas, chapter 1 also serves to introduce the material in the rest of the book.

Chapters 2 through 11 are for people who want to invest a bit more time to make higher-performance antennas. Chapters 2 through 4 feature some of the different antenna types and basics of antenna construction. Chapter 5 covers some simple antenna supports and masts. The antennas in the rest of the book are everything from basic designs to directional systems, and those that can be taken outside or hidden in a house or apartment.

The antenna designs in this book will open a door into the world of shortwave listening and will provide years of information and entertainment. This book takes a very basic approach to building antennas, so I hope that you will enjoy reading it and enjoy using the information within.

Shortwave basics

From reading some of the magazines and books that are currently available, it might seem as if everyone in the world thoroughly knows technical shortwave applications: propagation, antenna construction, and antenna theory. But, for some reason, the subject of shortwave radio has been held in the technical underground for decades. It's been a real mystery to most people. However, with new publicity, low prices and availability of equipment, and benefits of shortwave listening, many people are being introduced to shortwave radio.

Rather frequently, someone will see my portable radio and start asking questions. One of the most common is "You mean that radio can pick up stations from around the world?" So, I usually tune in the BBC or maybe Deutsche Welle and let the person listen a little. The next question is usually "You mean this is really coming from England?!" (or Germany, depending on which one I tuned in).

Although most of the people who work with shortwave on a regular basis take it for granted, the distances covered by shortwave radio stations are truly amazing. And it's not just huge government stations that get out this well, even small, portable ham stations, mini-powered private broadcasters, pirates, and clandestines can be heard around the world.

The methods by which shortwave radio signals travel from the transmitter are a bit different than those in the standard broadcast bands, and few people are familiar with these methods. As a result, it's important to at least have a background in shortwave propagation, broadcasting, and listening before you start building antennas. This way, you can understand why certain aspects (such as antenna length) are important.

Propagation

Before getting into construction techniques and simple antenna types, let's cover a bit about the basic characteristics of shortwave reception. Shortwave reception is an unpredictable, very complicated beast. The unpredictability is certainly one of the factors that attracted me to the hobby. It's exciting when you get a chance to hear stations that normally aren't audible in your region of the world.

Radio stations produce signals that take several different routes to reach listeners. The two main routes (although others do exist) are the ground wave and the sky wave. The *ground wave* is the radio wave that travels along the ground from the antenna tower. A good example of a ground wave is the signal that you can receive from a local AM broadcast station. The signal will generally be solid and fade-free. Actually, several different types of radio waves are considered ground waves, but (as mentioned earlier) this is a simplified discussion of radio propagation. The *sky wave*, on the other hand, is a component of the radio signal that shoots into the sky at a higher angle and is refracted by the *ionosphere* (covered in greater detail in the following paragraphs). The sky wave often can be heard thousands of miles away, depending on various conditions. Even strong sky wave signals often quickly fade down in strength, then return to the previous signal quality. This fading runs in cycles; depending on how fast or slow the fades occur, it could be either virtually unnoticeable or it could be quite bothersome.

Long-distance radio reception is possible because of one of the layers of our atmosphere, known as the ionosphere. The ionosphere is many miles above the earth, where the air is "thin"—containing few molecules. Here, the ionosphere is bombarded by x-rays, ultraviolet rays, and other forms of high-frequency radiation. This energy from the sun ionizes this layer by stripping electrons from the atoms.

The ionosphere can, in turn, be divided into several layers, but the D, E, and F layers are the ones that affect radio propagation. The D layer is closest to the surface of the earth. The existence and strength of this layer depends on, and is proportional to, the sun in the sky. As a result, the D layer gradually increases in strength in the morning, is strongest at midday, and gradually decreases until it disappears by nightfall. Also, the D layer is generally stronger in the summer than in the winter. On the lower frequencies (below about 10 MHz), the D layer absorbs any signals that are transmitted into it. A great example of this effect is to tune across the AM (mediumwave) broadcast band at midday and then do the same at night. At midday, you hear local stations and maybe a few powerful cross-state stations. But with nightfall, the band comes alive and stations from across the country are audible. You have just witnessed the effect of the D layer.

The E layer is much like the D layer, except that it is a bit higher and has a few redeeming characteristics. The E layer absorbs most radio signals, but it sometimes refracts shortwave signals—especially those above about 14 MHz. During the summer months, the higher frequency amateur bands are particularly "hot" during the daytime when the lower frequency bands are being eaten alive by the D and E layers. One of the most interesting characteristics of the E layer is called sporadic E skip. During the *sporadic E skip*, some higher frequencies in the lower VHF region, which don't normally skip, suddenly skip for very long distances. Sporadic E skip is somewhat common, but you have to be at the right place at the right time for a good opening. One time I lived in a small apartment and watched television on a small, beat-up black-and-white TV that my sister had given me. One severe disadvantage of using this TV was that my sister had broken off the whip antenna a few years earlier. It didn't receive that well, but we were close enough to Pittsburgh that a handful of stations would come in anyway. One evening at sunset, channel 4 from Pittsburgh started to fade out and was replaced by another signal. In a few minutes, KHAS, from Hastings, Nebraska, was in loud and clear. About 10 minutes later, KHAS was gone and the regular stations were back.

The F layer makes most shortwave and mediumwave skip possible. This layer is generally several hundred miles above the earth and remains ionized throughout much of the day and night. However, unlike the other layers (under most circumstances), the F layer refracts signals back to the earth. Because the F layer is so high above the earth, signals often skip over great distances—sometimes several thousand miles. As a result, it is possible to hear international broadcast stations with clear signals from around the world (Fig. I-1).

The ionosphere, skip conditions, and signal absorption have a number of peculiarities. One oddity is that frequencies above the shortwave bands normally penetrate the ionosphere and travel into space, but the lower shortwave frequencies are often absorbed by the ionosphere. As a result, there are no perfect frequencies—best frequencies depend on where the intended audience is, the time of the year, the condition of the ionosphere, etc. Another variable that dramatically affects listening is the skip distance. Long skip is not necessarily the most desirable condition. For example, it is common to listen to the 20-meter amateur band during the daytime

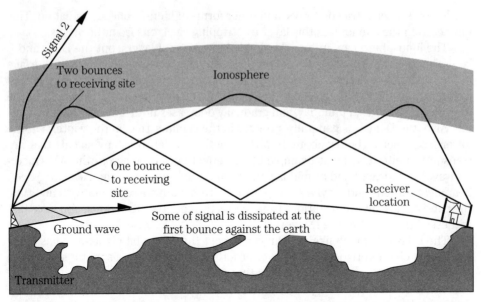

Signal 2

Two bounces
to receiving site

Ionosphere

One bounce
to receiving
site

Receiver
location

Some of signal is dissipated at the
first bounce against the earth

Ground wave

Transmitter

I-1 A simplified look at how shortwave radio signals can be received with help from the ionosphere.

hours and hear a station from a distant country, such as Australia, talking to someone in your state. The problem is that you will probably only hear the station in Australia, not the one in your state! Thus, if you are an amateur operator, you would try a frequency on a lower-frequency band if you wanted to contact someone that close.

The same holds true for broadcast listening. A number of U.S. private stations broadcast on the so-called 41-meter band. This area is fair to good for only close communications during the day, but at night the signals get out for thousands of miles. At night (at my location), these stations often drop to about half strength and they rapidly fade in and out. The problem is that I am too close to the transmitter for good reception at that time and most of the signal is skipping over me. These problems are virtually unheard of at AM (mediumwave) and FM broadcast frequencies, so most people are stunned that they occur on the shortwave frequencies.

One factor makes propagation forecasting and theory very complicated. As you know, shortwave signals are severely affected by the ionosphere, which is (in turn) affected by sunlight. Daylight and nightfall do not occur at the same time throughout the world. This creates some bizarre skip conditions, to say the least. The best way to see what frequencies are coming in at a particular time of day in your area is to either join a shortwave-listening club (so that you can see logs of what other people are hearing) or read the propagation forecasts in some of the amateur radio magazines. These methods are more valuable than simply trying to figure it out yourself.

This section has been a quick, superficial look at shortwave propagation—just something to acquaint you with how shortwave signals reach different parts of the world (Fig. I-2). As stated earlier, shortwave propagation is much more complicated

FROM F. C. NORFOLK, VA

Federal Communications Commission
Field Operations Bureau
Norfolk Office
1200 Communications Circle
Virginia Beach, Virginia 23455-3725

NEWS RELEASE   NEWS RELEASE

January 13, 1993

AMATEUR RADIO OPERATOR JAMS MARITIME RADIO
COMMUNICATION FREQUENCY ON EAST COAST

A marine radio frequency was jammed over much of the East Coast
since last Sunday (Jan. 10, 1993) by a mysterious signal that
interfered with a channel used for maritime communications.

Burkhart Monitoring Service, Richmond, VA heard a commercial FM
broadcast station on a shortwave radio frequency and alerted
Federal Communications Commission officials. Nationwide radio
long-range direction finding techniques--coordinated by the FCC's
Field Operations Bureau in Washington, D.C.--traced the signal to
the Elizabeth City, NC area. Agents dispatched by the FCC's
Norfolk Office last evening (Jan. 12, 1993) used mobile direction
finding equipment to locate the source of the offending signal.

J. J. Freeman, engineer in Charge of the Commission's Norfolk
Office said an amateur radio operator was using a 5 watt
transmitter to retransmit a local FM radio station from his "ham"
shack to his house, a few feet away. Retransmission of a commercial broadcast station is a violation of FCC rules.

Normally, a signal produced by such low power could not be
received more than 10 to 15 miles away. Freeman explained the
signal was causing interference at distant locations because of a
phenomenon known as "skip."

A recent and enduring weather pattern in the area set up conditions for "skip" to occur. In this case, as the weak signal was
transmitted, it was bouncing up and down against a cloud cover
that moved it along to places as far away as Allegan,
Michigan..... location of one of the Commission's monitoring
stations involved in the long range detection process.

The Norfolk Office has not yet completed its investigation of
this incident. For further information, call J. J. Freeman,
Engineer in Charge, at 804-441-6472.

I-2 Don't worry if you're having problems understanding the fine points of propagation. Sometimes even
the Federal Communications Commission fails to understand it! This news release includes a completely
erroneous description of radio propagation.

than this, and I left out many important terms and characteristics on purpose. A light section on the subject can help you to build better antennas. Too much information, on the other hand, can scare some people away—they think that the hobby is too complicated for them. Fact is, although many aspects of radio (including shortwave) and television are highly technical, you don't have to be an engineer to enjoy these mediums. For more detailed, yet easy-to-understand, coverage of shortwave propagation, see *The Practical Antenna Handbook—2nd Edition* by Joseph J. Carr.

1
CHAPTER

Beginner and makeshift antennas

When I was only 13, one of my friends picked up an ancient Hallicrafters SX-28A receiver. We spent many hours playing with this wondrous glowing monster and mysteriously hearing broadcasters from all over the world. It didn't take me long to know that this was the hobby for me.

Unfortunately, antennas were just as mysterious to me as the signals that were receivable on shortwave. I checked out a few antenna books, but all of them were loaded with complicated equations and construction techniques. I had almost no idea about relatively simple things, such as what type of wire to use, where to purchase coaxial cable, or what kind of connectors I should buy. After many failures and strange, near-hazardous situations in trees and on the roof of my parents' two-story house, I began to construct and install antennas that actually worked well.

This first chapter is dedicated to the days when my antennas were more useful as booby traps. If I had been able to find an extremely simple guide to antennas, rather than those that targeted the intermediate- or expert-level radio hobbyist, I might not have had such a difficult time getting started in the hobby.

Then again, if I hadn't had the experiences of being terribly confused for several years, breaking antennas, soldering elements improperly, misfiguring antenna lengths, and much more, I wouldn't be a capable, well-rounded shortwave listener, right? No way! Some things can be learned by reading, rather than "learning by experience." For example, just from what I have read, I know that I would never want to be burned at the stake. Standard antenna construction practices aren't quite this painful (maybe more on par with thumb screws), but you get the point.

Portable shortwave radios

Most of today's shortwave receivers are portables with built-in whip antennas. This type of antenna might appear to be a good substitute for an external antenna, but it isn't. With excellent portable radios, such as the Sangean ATS-803A and the Sony ICF-2010, using only the whip antenna results in a real loss of performance (similar to coupling a $1000 stereo to surplus 89¢ speakers). These two shortwave radios will perform on the same level as many tabletop radios that cost much more. But your radio is only as good as your antenna, and even the most basic shortwave program listeners should at least do some limited experimentation with external shortwave antennas.

These portable receivers with the built-in whip antennas are wonderful little creations. Only about 15 years ago they didn't exist. The closest thing to a portable shortwave radio was the venerable Yaesu FRG-7, a solid, heavy radio that ate D-cell batteries in a hurry. Also, today's portable radios are much more user-friendly—they are much easier to operate, have a boatload of memories, and have those helpful whip antennas. As a result of these features, even people who are not technically inclined can experience the benefits of listening to news, programs, and other things (alternative "pirate" radio, weather stations, military traffic, amateur stations, etc.) from around the world on their shortwave radios.

Many people now becoming involved in shortwave listening see it as a program service, not a hobby. In years past, shortwave radio listeners in North America were primarily licensed amateurs and radio junkies. The technical nature of the older literature and the complicated good-quality radios at that time created an invisible barrier that prevented many "nontechnical" people from enjoying the wonders of shortwave. Some amateurs and shortwave listeners seemed to enjoy the exclusive nature of the hobby, but all this has changed and now most everyone can enjoy shortwave.

I have read many antenna books that seem to cover the fine points of antenna construction more completely than the major points. For example, an antenna that receives well at 7 MHz (40 meters) should receive fairly well at 6 MHz and 8 MHz. Most antennas receive at least marginally well across a very large range of frequencies. Transmitting antennas are another story—an antenna that is cut for a different frequency than is being transmitted on can cause damage to the transmitter.

Another relative fallacy is "if you have a few kinks in your antenna, any bit of signal strength gained by the antenna will be lost in the kinks." The biggest problem of having kinks in your antenna is that the wire might snap as a result of the tension. Still, many people would have you believe that something catastrophic might happen or that your antenna is a total failure.

The important thing at this point is to get back to the basics. An antenna is necessary to receive signals. In the case of the portable radios with the built-in whip antennas, an external antenna should improve reception. Just how much the reception should improve depends on what it's worth to you to provide the auxiliary antenna. For example, when I go to my in-laws' house over the holidays, it's not worthwhile to me to install an elaborate antenna. I want to do some listening, but I don't want the time I would spend setting up an antenna to cut into the holiday festivities. So I settle on a low-class wire antenna that requires about 5 or 10 minutes for installation. It's not great, but it's much better than just using the whip antenna. Otherwise, when I plan to do more listening and when I have more time, it's worthwhile to spend more time and install a better, more complicated antenna.

Likewise, a traveling businessperson would not be able to build a proper shortwave antenna and use it on a regular basis. The setup time, space, and weight required would be prohibitive. Besides that, chances are that he or she would be planning only to catch the news or programming from one of the large, easily heard shortwave stations. This being the case, an antenna that could raise the signal level from fair to good is all that would be necessary. That is exactly what this chapter is all about: simple, quick antennas that can fill the minimum requirements for listening. If you do all of your listening at your house and if these antennas seem too simple or "low-brow" for your tastes, skip the antennas in this chapter and move on to those in the rest of the book.

Connections

It's very simple to attach antennas to the new breed of portable radios. Some portable radios (such as the Sangean ATS-803A) contain built-in jacks for plugging in external antennas for shortwave, some (such as the Sony ICF-2010) contain built-in jacks for plugging in external antennas for the radio bands other than shortwave, but most (such as the Sony ICF-SW30) don't contain any external antenna jacks.

The basic approach for connecting an external antenna to a portable receiver is to strip about 2" insulation off the end of a wire (most anything from #8 to #30, though the most popular antenna gauges are from #14 to #22) and wrap the stripped end around the end of the receiver's whip antenna (Fig. 1-1). If you want to impress your friends, you can use the proper term for this type of connection and tell them that the antenna is *directly coupled* to your radio. One problem with this method of antenna coupling is that it's easy to end up with an incomplete connection. Frequently rewrapping the end of your antenna around the radio's whip antenna to make sure that the connection is complete can become annoying.

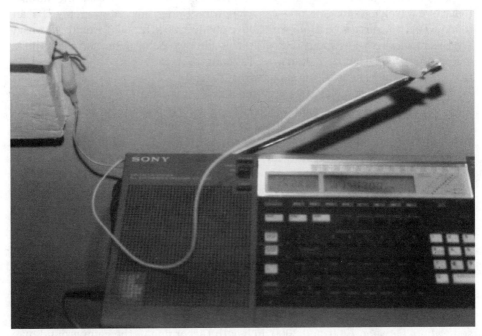

1-1 A wire antenna wrapped around the whip antenna of a portable receiver.

A solution to the connection problem is to pick up a pack of *clip leads* (also known as *test leads*) from an electronics store such as Radio Shack. Each lead is a different color and has an insulated alligator clip on each end. These leads are really handy to have around to make emergency connections. It's a good idea to buy a pack whether or not you want to use this as your main antenna connection arrangement.

To make a permanent antenna connection for a portable radio, solder a connector on the end of the antenna. For radios with an external antenna jack, your best choice is probably either a ¼" RCA plug or a ⅛" plug (like the kind used on headphones for portable stereos). Make sure you check what type of jack your radio has; otherwise, you might accidentally solder the wrong one on your antenna. For radios without the external shortwave antenna jack, a standard alligator clip is the best connector to solder to the antenna. For more information on soldering and construction techniques, see chapter 3, "Construction tools, materials, and practices."

The wire

The wire is the most basic form of antenna. The wire might not do everything well, but it does everything nonetheless. What I am calling the *wire* is simply a piece of wire, configured in whatever way. Unlike most antennas, the wire has no transmission line (used to carry signals from your antenna to your receiver) such as coaxial cable. This antenna functions as both the antenna and the transmission line.

Like most forms of horizontal and vertical antennas, the wire can be any length. However, a longer, relatively straight version of the wire would generally be considered a *longwire antenna*. When does the wire become a longwire? I would hesitate to call a 5' piece of wire a "longwire" antenna. Some sources say that any antenna that's one wavelength long or longer is a longwire. Under this criterion, my 125' antenna would be considered a longwire above about 7500 kHz and it would be considered a simple wire below about 7500 kHz. This sort of variable definition seems bulky and confusing for standard shortwave-listening purposes. Personally, I would say that anything over about 100' is a longwire antenna.

The receiving characteristics between a 100' longwire and a 1000' longwire are quite different, so if you're writing a reception report to a station or describing your antenna to someone, state the length of the antenna and the direction it is pointing. Wire antennas of less than 100' in length are much less directional in the way that they receive, so the direction in which shorter longwires are pointing is not as important for others to know.

As I mentioned, the receiving characteristics of a long longwire antenna are much different than those of a shorter wire antenna. The longer it is, the better it receives from each end of the antenna. Likewise, the longer it is, the less signal can be picked up from the sides of the antenna. This phenomenon occurs according to the proportion of antenna length to the wavelength (frequency) of the station that you're listening to. An extremely long longwire antenna might be a most incredible antenna for someone who only listens to a few small segments of the world.

For example, one weekend some friends and I got together to listen for low-power European shortwave pirate stations. We strung a longwire antenna that was somewhere between 1200' and 2000' in length (according to the campground map, the antenna was approximately 1700' long). The antenna was pointed to the northeast, right at Europe. As a result of our efforts, we heard several European pirate broadcasters with low power (only about 100 watts) and many North American pirates, including one local AM (mediumwave) pirate from New York City. In the case of the New York City AM pirate, it was booming in with excellent fidelity. I decided to try hearing the station with about 30 feet of wire a few hundred feet away. Nothing. The massive longwire made the difference between hearing nothing and hearing an excellent signal. On the other hand, we found that many of the North American stations had better signals with a simple inverted-V antenna because it was much less directional. As you can see, each antenna type has its advantages and disadvantages. It's all a matter of choice and taste.

One of the few drawbacks with today's crop of miniature portable shortwave sets is that the tiny electronics contained within the case are susceptible to electric currents—even signals within the radio. I have heard a handful of stories about one excellent portable. Because of the quality of the radio, many listeners DX (long-distance listen) with it. As a result, the longwire is a logical choice to connect to this radio for DXing. However, if the signal into the receiver is too strong, it can overload the front end of the receiver and POOF!, a semiconductor or two are rendered useless. In fact, you won't even see smoke, hear a blood-curdling explosion, or smell molten plastic. You'll only notice a significant drop in signal strength. Although the radio is repairable, the $50 (or so) bill per pop should be prohibitive. So, the warning is: *The longwire antenna could put your portable radio at risk. Be careful!* Just how long is too long? I haven't gone over 400' long with my portable receivers. Maybe I'm conservative with my antennas, but I like my radio and I like it to be working!

Thus far, the only version of the wire that I've covered in this section has been the outdoor longwire. The wire can also be used indoors, and it can be configured in different shapes. These antennas are the key types for portable shortwave radios on the market today.

As stated earlier in this chapter, you shouldn't worry about little details, such as antenna resonance or impedance, with these indoor makeshift antennas. The big concern is to get a length of wire up to "grab" as much signal as possible from the air. Crude as that might seem, it sure beats not having an antenna at all!

An indoor wire antenna can be held in place with thumbtacks, "discrete" tape, staples, or it could just be tied around a support (then stretched from support to support). Just remember that wires can be difficult to see and you might accidentally trip or "clothesline" an unsuspecting person. I made a handful of temporary antennas that hung at about eye level across a room. Although I almost always remembered that the antenna was there, I had a few experiences with walking into the wire and watching my portable receiver go flying off the table. It's not at all a pleasant situation, so please be careful when stringing wire—someone (or your receiver) could get injured.

You might also consider stringing the wire in a box-like shape. Considering that most rooms are in a box-like shape, it's easy enough just to run the wire along the contours of the walls. In general, most of these antennas will contain at least 35' of wire. An antenna like this can work fairly well, provided that it's not inside a metal-structured building and is not located near a large noise-generating source (such as fluorescent lights, "touch" lamps, microwave ovens, hair dryers, clothes dryers, etc.) while they are in operation.

I have had moderate success with these types of miniature indoor antennas. I enjoy listening to music, news, or sports while I'm working, so they have been particularly useful. For this type of simple program listening, these antennas often made the difference between success or failure at being able to understand the BBC news over the sound of running water at the sink while I washed dishes. As you might expect, these indoor wires are poor DX antennas—I have had a few good catches while using them, but these were rare and more based on extraordinary propagational conditions than on good antenna performance.

The reel antenna

One of the most practical new developments in shortwave-listening antenna technology (or gadgetry) is the *reel antenna*. The reel antenna is basically a handy version of the indoor wire that is neat and easy to carry. The actual wire antenna is held inside a reel. The other end of the wire has a small clip (somewhat similar to the type used to clip on chip bags), which you can clip onto the end of a whip antenna.

I received a commercial version of a reel antenna from one of my friends. I love this antenna because I can wind it in immediately after a brief program-listening session in the kitchen. Because the regular wires were more of a bother to install and wrap up, I would normally leave them strung up. The wire usually crossed the kitchen cabinets and every time we reached for a plate or a glass, we were in danger of setting off my booby trap. The reel antenna ended nearly all of these problems for me.

So why am I writing about the virtues of a commercially made antenna in a book about building your own antennas? The reel antenna has one flaw—it's very short and it works for only the most basic listening. What I wanted to experiment with was constructing longer reel antennas—antennas that could actually be used for light- to heavy-duty DXing.

The first problem was finding an appropriate reel. I didn't really want to modify a commercial reel antenna because it seemed to defeat the ingenuity of the experiment. I thought about using a fishing reel (fishing reel antennas have appeared in the hobby press for several decades), but I felt that it would be too bulky and would probably unwind into a mass of knots while I was taking it on a trip. My choice for an appropriate reel was a standard chalk line, like those used in house construction.

I don't know how many people have old chalk lines sitting in their basements and garages, waiting to be converted into portable antennas. However, I would guess that few people do. A new chalk line isn't terribly expensive. In fact, I picked mine up for about $4, much cheaper than a commercially produced reel antenna.

The huge advantage of using a new chalk line is that it hasn't yet been filled with chalk dust. If you choose a used chalk line to convert into a reel antenna, you must rinse it out several times with water. Otherwise, every time you unwind the antenna, the wire will be covered with chalk dust and bits of dust will spill out inside the house. Using a dusty chalk line for a reel antenna might work well for a vacuum cleaner ad on TV, but the resulting mess sure isn't fun in real life.

To build my reel antenna, I first pulled the string out of a new chalk line case until the reel was completely unwound. Then, I removed the screws in the case of the chalk line and pulled it apart. The string was easy to get to on the plastic spool, so I cut it off with a pair of scissors. Next, I got the wire I was planning to use, ran it through the spool, and knotted it. I used standard #20 stranded hookup wire with rubber insulation. After winding about 50 feet of wire onto the reel, I cut off the wire, stripped about an inch of insulation off the exposed end, and soldered on an alligator clip. The case can be screwed back together anytime after you knot the wire inside of the spool.

I often stick up longwire antennas in the winter when I visit my parents over the holidays. Invariably, I end up with a massive knot in my wire about 75 feet from the house and spend about an hour attempting to untangle the wire with numb hands in 10°F weather. After building the reel antenna, a lightbulb popped up over my head, and I imagined how convenient it would be to have a longwire reel antenna.

For the longwire reel antenna, I used very light gauge (approximately #26) enamelled wire. I chose this type of wire because it has a very small diameter and quite a bit of it could be held on a chalk line reel (Fig. 1-2). Also, the insulation is very hard and slick and is less apt to jam up the reel. I was surprised to find that I could fit well over 300' of wire on the reel without having any winding problems.

1-2 A reel antenna.

The procedure for building the longwire reel antenna is the same as that for building the standard reel, except that I didn't use an alligator clip on the end. I was afraid that the clip would break off because of the light gauge of the wire, so I tied the end of the wire around the old end of the chalk line (to prevent the antenna from getting wound inside the case). Then I moved down the wire about an inch and carefully scraped off the enamel insulation for about an inch. When the antenna went up, I connected an alligator clip lead to the place where the insulation was removed on the antenna and connected the other end to the whip antenna of the portable shortwave receiver.

The reel antennas perform on par with standard wire and longwire antennas of equal length. The whole benefit of using a reel antenna is merely in the ease of installing and dismantling. However, in my first winter experience with the longwire reel, I wound it up in less than 15 minutes—even though it ran through trees and into the woods, was covered with snow and ice, and it was several hours after sunset. I was pleased. I find the prospect of spending more time keeping warm while listening, and less time freezing in snowstorms, rather exciting!

The self-sticking screen antenna

The wire antenna and the reel version of the wire are excellent portable antennas. However, both are totally ineffective inside of a metal-structured building, such as a motel, trailer, or office building. In these cases, it would be best to have an antenna installed outside. I have a friend who worked in an office building and his shortwave reception was terrible because the steel structure shielded out radio signals. He stealthily ran a very fine gauge of enamelled wire from his desk out through a window in the office building, and along a crack in the building to the ground floor. Although the system worked well, someone eventually found the antenna and removed it.

The bottom line is that using an outdoor antenna from a public building could cause you problems with your job, or you could wind up facing a lawsuit (if, for example, someone trips as a result of an antenna that you installed at a motel).

The only good location for an indoor antenna in a steel-structured building is at a window, where only glass is between the antenna and the great outdoors. A 3' wire antenna is impractically short at shortwave frequencies, so that rules out the standard wire and vertical antennas. Surprisingly, one of the best makeshift antennas for this awkward predicament is a piece of window screen.

Window screen antennas have occasionally appeared in hobby publications over the past decade or two. In these publications, the window screen was normally assumed to be in the window. However, it seems that in most of the cases where this type of antenna would be necessary, there is no screen in the window. Also, with the "wonders of modern technology," most of the newer window screens are made out of plastic, not metal. Because plastic does not conduct electricity, plastic window screens cannot be used as antennas.

For people who travel on business and still want to catch the latest news and other programming on shortwave, it might be convenient to carry a portable window screen antenna (Fig. 1-3). Essential to this antenna is (obviously) a piece of window screen. In the ratio of size and performance versus convenience, a best bet for the size of this antenna would be between 1' × 2' and 2' × 3'.

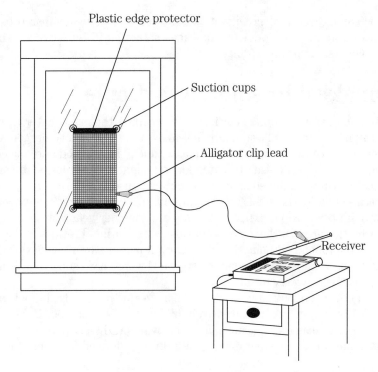

Plastic edge protector

Suction cups

Alligator clip lead

Receiver

1-3 A window screen antenna.

Try the local hardware store or construction supply center for window screen. Most of these stores sell various grades of window screen on large rolls. Once again, make sure that you use metal screen, not plastic screen. Either cut the piece to the size that you want or have it cut to size by a store clerk.

Afterward, you can place duct tape around all of the sides, except for a ½" gap along one of the sides. The duct tape around the edges will prevent you from cutting yourself or other objects while using or transporting the antenna. The small gap in the duct tape is where an alligator clip lead should be placed to connect the screen antenna to the whip antenna of the receiver. You might instead choose to seal all of the sides with duct tape (not leaving a gap for an alligator clip) and solder a wire directly to the screen. I didn't choose this means of connecting the screen antenna to the receiver because the solder connection would be rather fragile. I can just imagine a solder joint getting crushed and breaking under a stack of books.

The next step is to find some small suction cups at a craft store. Lately, there has been a proliferation of small suction cups that are used for such things as hanging sun catchers on house windows and hanging Garfield dolls in car windows. Just fasten one of these suction cups on each corner of the antenna and it's ready to hang!

When I constructed my version of this antenna, I used an old piece of metal screen that I found behind the wall in our laundry room. The screen was dirty and slightly corroded, so I wire brushed the area where I was going to connect the alligator clip. Cleaning this area of the screen will ensure a good contact between the clip lead and the screen.

As you can expect, the screen antenna performs dismally compared to a standard outdoor antenna. But it does work somewhat and it is fairly effective if you're stuck in a metal-structured building.

The makeshift solderless dipole

Like the longwire mentioned earlier in this chapter, the makeshift solderless dipole is a simplified version of a standard antenna. In the case of an emergency or disaster when the power is out, the means to assemble a quick, good antenna could be life-saving. Even if your life isn't threatened, you might try the makeshift solderless dipole in cases where you need an antenna but can't use a soldering iron.

A typical scenario where this type of antenna is useful is in my hometown. When I was growing up, we could expect a few snowstorms per year that dropped more than 10". Chances are that the winds would also whip during this time, and we would end up snowbound and without electricity for a few hours or a few days. Often my outdoor antenna would be downed in the storm—I would have supplies to make new antennas, but no electricity to solder with.

Before I cover the makeshift dipole, take a look at the standard dipole antenna (which is featured much more extensively in chapter 7). It is one of the best and most popular antennas for transmitting or receiving on the shortwave frequencies. In fact, most antennas are either directly or indirectly derived from the standard dipole.

The standard dipole is an antenna that has two equal-length elements that are connected to the radio equipment via a two-wire line or a coaxial cable. The total length of the antenna elements is generally ½ wavelength long (at the frequency range that you are interested in listening to). The dipole is slightly directional (in all directions) at angles that are perpendicular to the antenna.

In order to make this solderless antenna (Fig. 1-4), you must first have an appropriate length of coaxial cable. What length is appropriate depends on how you situate your antenna and your receiver. If you were about to install your antenna in an attic with your receiver in the center of the room, you would probably need less than

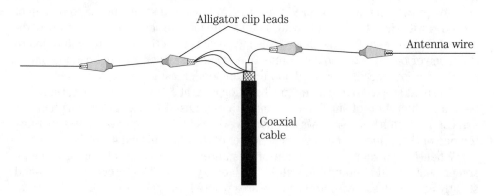

1-4 The makeshift solderless dipole antenna.

10' of coaxial cable. On the other hand, if your radio was on the other side of the room or if the antenna was to be located in the attic and the radio was downstairs, you would need much more coax. Next, you need a connector to attach the antenna to your radio. If you have a small portable receiver, you need an alligator clip. In this case, cut away about an inch of the coaxial cable, except for the center conductor. Then connect an alligator clip lead between the center conductor and the whip antenna of the portable receiver (Fig. 1-5).

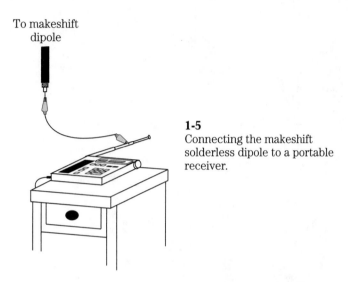

To makeshift
dipole

1-5
Connecting the makeshift solderless dipole to a portable receiver.

If you have a larger radio, you could use the antenna jack. The most common antenna plug for shortwave equipment is the PL-259 connector (available at any electronics parts store or mail-order supplier). If you plan to use a PL-259 connector for this sort of project, you must get solderless connectors. With solderless connectors, you only need to remove a "proper" amount of the outer sheathing, copper braid, and inner dielectric (see chapter 3 and Fig. 3-6 for more information). Then, you can slide the PL-259 over the end and crimp the end closed with a pair of pliers.

As far as the other end is concerned, about two inches of the outer sheathing should be cut off with a knife (be sure not to cut into the wire braid). Then, unbraid down one side of the braided shield. When you are finished, twist the braid together into one thick 2" long piece of wire. Next, move down an inch from the end of the coaxial cable and remove the inner dielectric, leaving one inch of the center conductor exposed.

For the antenna elements, connect one alligator clip lead to the thick twisted shield (ground side) and connect a different alligator clip lead to the center conductor. The "free" ends of these two alligator clip leads should each be clipped to a separate length of wire and installed.

If you want to make the antenna match as closely as possible to the frequency range that you plan to listen to, use the chart in the section on building dipoles in chapter 7 to cut the antenna elements to the appropriate length.

I don't presently live in an area that gets struck by many severe snowstorms every year. Fortunately, we rarely lose power, so I have done little experimenting with this antenna. It seems to work fairly well, but I don't know what effect the alligator clip leads have on the length of the resonant elements. I suppose that if your electrical service is constantly in question and if you don't have any prebuilt backup antennas, you might want to experiment with what lengths work best for these antennas. On the other hand, it would be easier to build a backup emergency dipole for such situations.

2
CHAPTER

SWL requirements

The procedures involved in building different shortwave listening antennas are more numerous than the selection of ice cream at Baskin-Robbins. A vast range of frequencies fall within the term *shortwave;* the listener's interests will dictate what type of antenna is necessary. Shortwave frequencies extend from 1700 kHz (the top of the AM broadcast band) to 30 MHz (a bit above the top of the citizen's band). No single practical-sized antenna can be effective over this broad frequency range. Some, however, perform reasonably well over large portions of the SWL bands.

Two basic types of antennas are the *horizontal* (mounted parallel to the earth) and the *vertical* (mounted perpendicular to the earth). The horizontal antenna vaguely resembles a clothesline. On the other hand, the vertical antenna is similar to a flagpole. There are many variations of these two antenna types (including some that exhibit both vertical and horizontal characteristics), but most SWL systems usually lean toward one of these two categories.

Horizontal antennas

The horizontal antenna is supported at both ends and can be fed to the receiver in many ways. Figure 2-1 shows the various means of feeding the signal to the receiver: (2-1A) end feed, (2-1B) center feed, and (2-1C) off-center feed. A larger space is generally required to install a horizontal antenna than is required by its vertical counterpart. However, it is usually much easier and safer to install an 80' *long* antenna than it is to install an 80' *tall* antenna.

For best performance, the horizontal antenna system should be mounted perfectly horizontal to the earth. However, as a result of space, structural, and natural limitations, this ideal installation is often unattainable. Like many things, it's tough to score a perfect antenna in an imperfect world. It's a better strategy to reduce the amount of imperfections in an antenna than to aim for the perfect antenna. Besides, the differences in performance between a good, but imperfect, antenna and an excellent one will probably not be noticed by the average shortwave listener. Specific antenna projects using the horizontal design method are covered in later chapters, and the specific problems that might be encountered are explained.

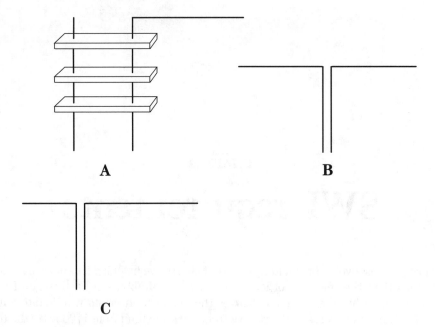

2-1 The different methods of feeding a wire antenna: A) end feed, B) center feed, and C) off-center feed.

Generally speaking, twice as much antenna wire length is required to mount a proper horizontal antenna system than is required for a vertical antenna system that is designed to cover the same range of frequencies. Horizontal antenna systems best receive transmitted signals that originate from a horizontal antenna. However, most transmitted signals carry a horizontal and a vertical component. This holds true regardless of the type of antenna system that was used to transmit the signal. Some people experiment with both horizontal and vertical antenna systems to improve the chances of receiving the signals clearly.

Horizontally polarized antennas are usually used by amateur radio operators when they operate from fixed positions (i.e., at home, field day, or vacationing). However, most mobile operations (amateur, business, CB, commercial, or military) exclusively use vertical whip antennas. Standard commercial mediumwave (AM) stations also use the vertical antenna, and most commercial FM stations use a combination of vertical and horizontal systems. Your own preferences are the deciding factor in what type of antenna system to install.

Vertical antennas

Most everyone has seen a vertical antenna of some sort; it's tough to go anywhere and *not* see one! A few of the common applications for vertical antennas include: cellular and cordless telephones; mobile AM and FM car antennas (Fig. 2-2); AM, FM, and television transmitting antennas (Fig. 2-3); and CB antennas.

2-2
A car whip antenna.

2-3
A mediumwave (AM broadcast band) antenna.

In most cases, vertical antenna systems require only half the wire length of a horizontal system. The earth itself or a manufactured radial ground system usually makes up for the missing half of the antenna. The center conductor of the coaxial cable (or one side of the twin-lead or open-wire transmission line) is connected to the vertical portion of the antenna and the coaxial shield (or other side of the twin-lead or open-wire transmission line) is connected to an earth ground.

Like antennas, grounds can also be improved upon. Unless you live in a salt marsh (which has extremely high ground conductivity), you might consider improving the ground's electrical conductivity by installing a series of uninsulated copper or aluminum wires that are at least ¼ wavelength long, radiating in a horizontal pattern from the base of the antenna. These wires should be buried a few inches beneath the soil.

Be careful if using ground radials in a residential location. Depending on the situation, you could be in danger of striking underground cables or pipes. Also be aware of the potential social difficulties that can occur when an enthusiastic radio hobbyist seeks the perfect ground system. I have heard a few tales of suburban antenna builders who removed all of the grass in their yard (so that a huge spider web of ground radials could be set into the ground) to the great dismay of the spouse and neighbors. The conflicts that could result from installing an excellent ground system could be more damaging to your shortwave listening than merely tolerating a less-than-perfect ground system!

The vertical antenna should be located as far as possible from any large surrounding objects (especially such things as steel towers, power lines, and aluminum-sided buildings) in order to obtain a clear signal path. Vertical antennas are usually considered omnidirectional, receiving signals from all directions. In some instances, vertical antennas have performed more efficiently than horizontal systems in the reception of signals from distant places around the world.

When installing a vertical antenna system, an overhanging branch from a tall tree (Fig. 2-4) or other structure can be used as an anchoring point for the antenna wire, which can then be dropped to a point a few inches above the ground. The antenna wire or element should be as close to vertical as possible. However, antennas with slight variances still provide satisfactory operation. The end of the antenna closest to the ground is fed to the receiver by a transmission line, one side of which is connected to a ground rod or other grounding system that lies directly beneath the antenna. The importance of a good grounding system cannot be emphasized enough for most vertical antennas. A good ground provides the additional advantage of increased lightning protection.

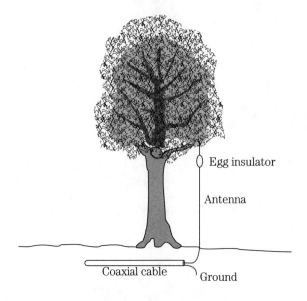

Egg insulator

Antenna

Coaxial cable   Ground

2-4
A vertical antenna installed in an overhanging tree.

Transmission lines

The signals that are intercepted by the antenna are carried to the receiver by means of a transmission line, which is sometimes referred to as a *feed line*. It can consist of one end of the antenna itself, a two-wire flat cable (much like or even the same as that which is used for hookups to television antennas), or a length of coaxial cable, which has a solid center wire or conductor that is surrounded and insulated from a braided outer conductor. Some transmission line applications require the line to pick up a portion of the signals, others use it to carry signals from the antenna to the receiver only. Transmission line quality is of paramount importance—especially when a considerable distance lies between the antenna site and the receiver location. A poor-quality line induces signal losses between the antenna and the receiver. These signal losses result in poor reception of weaker signals—some might not be audible. When using transmission line other than coaxial cable, you must take care to separate the line from any large objects by several inches. A line that lies against the side of a house, a tree, or any metal object does not provide the best signal transfer from the antenna to the receiver. Some of the less-expensive types of transmission lines are intended for indoor installation only and deteriorate rapidly when exposed to moisture. Even when high-quality lines are used, periodic inspection for breaks in the outer insulation is necessary. Any moisture that enters a transmission line through a crack in the insulation renders the entire length of cable useless in a short period of time.

Transmission lines differ greatly in their construction and in the type of applications for which they are designed. Some of the more common types are the *single-wire line*, *insulated two-wire line*, *coaxial cable*, *shielded pair*, *twisted pair*, and *open two-wire line*.

Single-wire line

Single-wire line is the simplest type of transmission line (Fig. 2-5). It consists of a single-wire conductor between the antenna element and the receiver. A single-wire line might be difficult to match with the input of many of the more complex shortwave receivers without the aid of an antenna tuner. This transmission line is generally used in applications where its simplicity and ease of installation outweigh its inefficiency.

Insulated two-wire line

Insulated two-wire transmission line (also known as *twin-lead*) is commonly used (Fig. 2-6). The cable consists of two conductors, which are separated from each other by a flat strip of plastic insulation. The entire assembly is encased in a flexible plastic, which insulates the two conductors from contact with foreign objects. This type of line is easy to work with and install and can be bent around corners with no fear of a conductor breaking.

Coaxial cable

A transmission line can be fabricated by placing one conductor within another. This type is called a *coaxial cable*; it usually consists of a wire conductor placed in

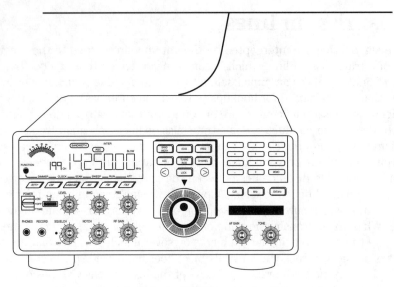

2-5 A single-wire transmission line.

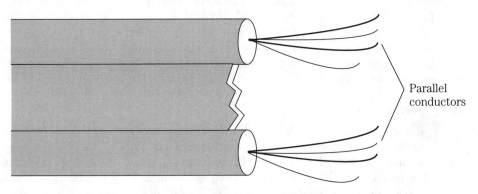

Parallel
conductors

2-6 Twin-lead transmission line.

the middle of a flexible roll of braided copper wire (Fig. 2-7). The inner conductor is kept an equal distance from the outer through the use of nonconducting spacers or a solid coating of insulation. High-grade coaxial lines can be used throughout the entire shortwave frequency range with excellent signal transfer between the antenna and the receiver. Coax is the most popular type of transmission line for shortwave receivers and antennas.

Shielded pair

When an insulated two-wire transmission line is placed inside a flexible roll of metal or braided copper wires, it is called a *shielded pair* (Fig. 2-8). Construction is

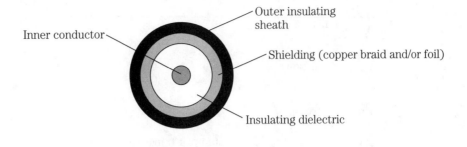

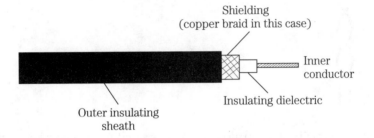

2-7 A breakdown of coaxial cable.

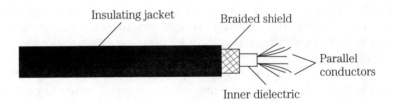

2-8 Shielded pair transmission line.

very similar to that of coaxial line, but the two conductors are encased within an outer conductor, which is usually covered with plastic insulation. The shielded-pair transmission line is more stable in operation than the basic two-wire line and it has the advantage of being more immune to noise pick-up from outside electrical sources.

Twisted pair

Two insulated wires can be twisted together to form a flexible type of transmission line (Fig. 2-9). No spacing materials are required because each wire is insulated over its entire length. The twisted-pair transmission line is limited to uses when the distance between the antenna and receiver is extremely short.

The twisted pair is an antiquated type of transmission line. It was used frequently before World War II, but since that time it has been virtually replaced by coaxial cable. As a result of the high signal losses that are incurred by the use of twisted-pair transmission line, it is very seldom utilized in shortwave applications.

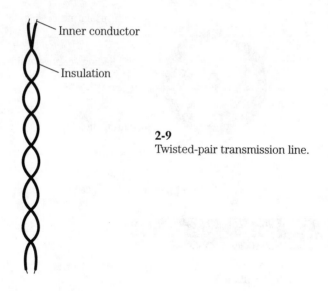

2-9
Twisted-pair transmission line.

Still, it is included in this book for true experimenters and for people who operate vintage equipment and who want to have a vintage-type antenna.

Open two-wire line

Also called a *parallel conductor line* and *ladder line*, the *open two-wire line* (Fig. 2-10) is identical to the insulated two-wire described earlier, but instead of a plastic spacer and insulation coating, short ceramic insulators are used every few inches to keep the two conductors an equal distance apart at all points in the line. The open two-wire line is difficult to work with because the spacing between the two conductors tends to change when the line is bent around a corner or positioned to bypass any large objects. A slight change in the spacing of a portion of the line results in increased signal losses at the receiver.

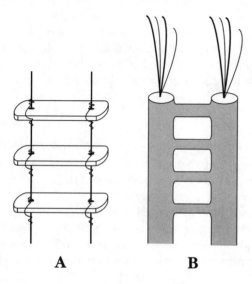

2-10
Ladder transmission line: (A) 600-Ω open line and (B) 450-Ω commercially made ladder line.

A   **B**

Selecting an antenna

By now, you can probably see that there is no overall perfect antenna for all situations. Every type of antenna has its own particular advantages and disadvantages. The installation of most shortwave antennas is a relatively inexpensive undertaking, and it really does not require a great deal of time if the original planning has been well thought out.

If a particular antenna site encompasses a relatively small area, a vertical antenna might be ideal. On the other hand, if a great deal of space is available (especially if there are trees, poles, or other supports at the outer edges of the mounting site), a horizontal antenna that is connected to one of these supports might fill the bill. Before constructing any antenna system, carefully plan exactly what you want and how you want to install it. Pay specific attention to antenna wire length, supports, and heights required above ground. The last thing you want to have happen is to get halfway through the antenna installation, only to find that the coaxial cable isn't long enough . . . or that the antenna is longer than the land that you're putting it on. These types of errors are not uncommon!

Some of the most complex antenna systems described in later chapters can be erected for under $30. In fact, you might already have required materials on hand. If this is a first-time antenna project for you, it is best to start with a relatively simple antenna system (such as the antennas in chapter 1) and modify it as your skills and needs increase.

Most of the projects in this book can be completed over a weekend or even in a few hours. You should purchase all materials before you start the project and allow a reasonable length of time for its completion. Don't rush! You could make mistakes or improper connections, which would require additional time for correction.

Safety

Although antenna construction is generally extremely safe, antenna installation can be quite dangerous. Depending on how you install your antennas, you could run the risk of lethal injuries from falling out of trees or off houses and towers.

Another extreme danger with antenna installation is electrocution. Each year antenna enthusiasts are seriously injured or killed when antennas come in contact with high-voltage cables. Don't run the risk of electrocution by attempting to install an antenna system that is too large for adequate power-line clearance. Always keep your antenna away from electrical power lines!

3
CHAPTER

Construction tools, materials, and practices

Tools

Before you attempt to build any project, you should have the correct tools and materials available. Antenna systems are no exception. Some common tools include: pliers, sidecutters, a pair of long-nose (or needle-nose) pliers, and (depending on the project) a hammer and a medium-sized screwdriver. A good grade of rosin-core solder and a medium- to heavy-wattage soldering gun complete the antenna builder's basic tool box. Other equipment that might be handy includes an inexpensive ohmmeter for testing transmission lines for breaks and shorts and a small assortment of alligator clips for temporarily securing small wires. Some antenna systems might require a special tool or two, but this assortment is generally adequate for the majority of home antenna construction projects.

Antenna materials

Materials required for each project in this book are listed with the building instructions. Always use copper wire (or copper-covered wire) when building antenna systems. Aluminum wire is less expensive and usually easier to work with, but it presents soldering problems—nothing seems to stick to it! Aluminum also tends to oxidize and connections often break after a short period of use. If you decide to use aluminum anyway, remember to wire brush the areas to be soldered. After the joint has been soldered, it must be waterproofed with a silicone sealant or electrical tape to prevent the joint from oxidizing and breaking apart. Many of the illustrations in this book do not show the sealant so that you can see how to make the connections. Aluminum wire is excellent when used for buried ground systems because it is inexpensive and because the grounds radials are stationary—which does not place stress on the joints.

Ceramic, glass, or plastic insulators (Fig. 3-1) should be used at the feedpoint and ends of wire antennas. Today, plastic insulators are the most common and they are quite inexpensive—usually less than 80¢ apiece. Glass insulators were most common in the early days of radio, and ceramic insulators were used for the many years between then and the present.

3-1 A glass center insulator (bottom) and a plastic "dog bone" insulator.

Some SWL antenna builders have spent hours of time and effort removing the rubber or plastic insulation from copper wire that was designed for electrical wiring purposes, in belief that the antenna wire must be bare in order to achieve proper reception. This assumption is completely false. Actually, the rubber insulation helps to prevent a corrosive build-up on the wire. In turn, others are misled to believe that this copper tarnish prevents signals from reaching their antennas. I have even heard about hobbyists who pull down their antennas periodically to sand off the tarnish! No type of rubber, plastic, or enamel insulation affects the performance of your receiving antenna in the least.

Most tools and materials required to build shortwave antenna systems can be found in any hardware or hobby store. Another excellent source of antenna materials, insulators, and accessories is a surplus electronics catalog. Here, you'll not only find the basic elements required, but also a healthy listing of adjustable coils, antenna switches, relays, etc. You might even get an idea for a modification or an improvement to your newly built antenna system that will customize it to suit your individual operating needs.

Don't run out and start spending money before checking the basement, attic, garage, or other area where your extra supplies are stored. If you don't find exactly what the instructions call for, improvise a little, while still adhering to basic antenna-building principles. If you are not certain of a substitution material, try it anyway. If the end product, proper reception, is achieved, then your choice was a wise one; if it doesn't work, try something else. I've heard stories about listeners who have successfully used their rain gutters as antennas, and hams who have successfully made radio contacts on bed springs, TV antennas, and barbed-wire fences.

If you live in an older house, it's hard to say what you might find. Friends of mine once asked me to dismantle an antenna from the attic of the house they had just bought. In the attic of the large Victorian was a pre-1940-style three-wire antenna, complete with dirty, tarnished #14 copper wire and seven glass insulators. Although I hated to destroy a piece of history from about 60 or 70 years ago, I knew it all had to go. Even though the antenna is no longer in its original configuration, at least the wire and insulators are being used in my antennas.

Aside from houses, another good place to look for antenna-building materials is at hamfests. Hamfests are regional amateur radio events where companies and dealers display new equipment, amateurs can take their radio license tests, and participants can attend seminars on various radio topics. Most hamfests also have an extensive flea market area. I have seen some great deals on wire, connectors, coaxial cable, and even damaged antennas that need some fix-up work at flea markets.

You can successfully substitute materials and still achieve excellent results, but substituting or changing calculated antenna wire lengths degrades the antenna's performance. An antenna system that is designed to operate at a certain frequency must have the physical length described in order for it to work properly. Your antenna will not work as well if it's appreciably shorter or longer than the calculated length. Think of the antenna as the string of a guitar or violin. When that string is a certain length, it plays a particular note. When the string is shortened by pressing it against the fret board, a different note is achieved. Consequently, when the length of an antenna is changed, the note, or frequency it is designed to receive, will also change.

Antenna supports

Mechanical supports are required for some of the antenna projects covered in later chapters. Your local hardware store is the first place to look for aluminum tubing. Electrical conduit can be used in some instances, but thin-wall aluminum has the advantage of providing a great deal of rigid strength yet still being exceptionally light. Because aluminum tubing is so lightweight, it is much easier to install. If you plan to build these types of antennas, you also need a small assortment of couplers for splicing lengths of tubing. These should also be available at most hardware stores.

If you can't use a tree or the roof of your house as antenna supports, and you still want an outdoor antenna, you probably need to buy or build an antenna support, mast, or tower. Chapters of this book contain a few ideas and tips on building your own antenna supports that should be helpful. If you decide to take that route, a local lumber supplier should have what you need for antenna supports. If you need special dimensions or cut-outs for your project, the lumber company generally has the various saws and woodworking equipment to customize your purchase on the spot.

One point that might be on par with your mom telling you to wash behind your ears is: Remember to purchase all of the materials for a project before starting it. If you only have the materials for a portion of the completed system, you might lose the drive required for completion while waiting for the missing parts. I have real problems with antenna projects that I have only partially completed. These projects wind up sitting in a corner for a while until they become too much of a nuisance, then, in the process of housecleaning, they get moved to the attic. There, coils of wire get shifted into different boxes and lost, or I forget which wires were cut for what piece. I need to do the entire project in a weekend or I waste my time and resources. I would imagine that a number of other people have this problem, too.

Permissions

If you live in an apartment complex or a neighborhood with strict zoning requirements, check with the landlord or zoning officials before ordering materials for your antenna. If you present a harmless appearance, use proper diplomacy, and give an explanation or drawing of what you plan to erect, most reasonable people will work with you. Some might be so interested in what you're doing that they'll offer to give you a hand with the construction project.

There are ways in which shortwave listeners can bypass strict or unreasonable landlords or apartment managers, although I don't necessarily recommend these methods. Some apartment dwellers have installed antennas inside PVC flag poles, dropped wire antennas out of windows at night, and used other clandestine methods to install an outdoor antenna. When I was in college, I ran a wire out the window and across a neighbor's garage roof. Looking back on the situation, I realize that I should have talked to the owner of the garage. The wire antenna wasn't easy to spot, and at the time, I figured that it wasn't hurting anyone and nobody would see it anyway.

This type of logic could cause problems with your neighbors or even get you booted out of an apartment. Without a proper knowledge of what's going on, many people seem to suspect shortwave listeners (running around with wires and tubing and climbing trees) of espionage or some other nasty crime. So ask for permission to install antennas. You might actually interest a few people in the wonders of shortwave radio.

Care of tools

You can save much time and effort if you maintain your tools regularly. If you are really ambitious, inspect your tools a few days before you intend to start working on a project. Dull cutting pliers and drill bits can delay a project for a week, if, like many hobbyists, your work must be confined to weekends. If you go ahead and use the tools, you run the risk of leaving ragged edges or breaking whatever you cut or drill. Drill bits and all tools with cutting edges should be sharpened regularly. Constant grinding or cutting with a dull tool or bit takes more time and wears out the working surfaces that much faster.

Before you solder a connection, make absolutely certain that you have a good mechanical joint. Never place two wires together and depend on the solder to connect the two. Solder can only provide a good electrical connection; mechanically, it's very weak. Always wrap the wires tightly around each other with a pair of pliers and examine the unsoldered joint by pulling slightly at the connection. If anything moves, wrap it tighter. Only when you notice no movement should you begin the soldering work. A few patient moments of practice at making proper solder connections will almost surely save you hours of headaches in the future.

Soldering irons perform faithfully if the soldering tip is kept well tinned with solder. Don't use more heat than is necessary for the job and avoid unnecessary pressure between the tip and the object to be soldered. Improper soldering accounts for a large majority of the failures in homebuilt kits, electronic projects, and antennas. A clean soldering joint should always be obtained before applying the tip of the iron. The secret then is to use the correct amount of heat. If the joint is not heated to a high enough temperature, the result will be a cold solder joint. This is solder that has melted at a temperature that was not high enough to properly heat the joint. Signs of this condition are dull, rough-looking blobs of solder (Fig. 3-2). A proper solder joint is smooth and shiny. To achieve this, apply the soldering tip and the solder to the joint at the same time; wait until solder starts to flow into the joint, then remove the tip and examine the joint immediately to see if the solder still seems to be molten. Quick examination is necessary because a properly soldered joint cools in a second or two. If the solder is still molten upon examination, you will see a change on its surface as it dries (Fig. 3-3).

3-2 A cold solder joint.

Again, a dull, rough-looking blob of solder means a cold solder joint and trouble. A smooth and shiny joint is a sign of proper soldering technique and stable operation from your homebuilt project. Much antenna soldering can be done in the shop, but some of it must be performed at an out-of-doors site. Soldering in a mild wind is often difficult, if not impossible, because of the cooling effects. In this situation, bring the solder joint in close to your body (while still maintaining a safe distance) and shield it with your back to the wind.

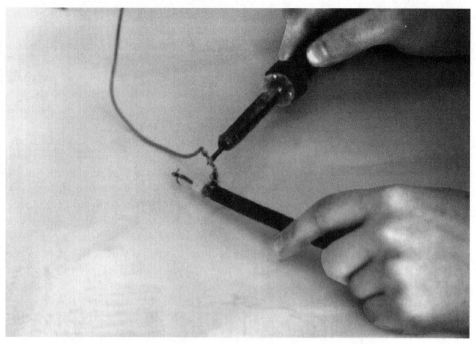

3-3 Making a good solder joint.

Coil winding

Some of the projects in this book require the construction of *loading coils*. A loading coil is just what its name implies: a coil of wire that is used to "load" antennas. A loading coil is normally used with antennas that are physically short to make them electrically seem as if they are the proper length for the frequency.

Proper coil winding requires a coil form, which can consist of anything from a pencil to a beer can. No coils required in any of these construction projects need to be perfect, but proper construction results in more consistent operation and your finished product will be more appealing to the eye. The coil form should be slightly smaller in diameter than the required diameter of the finished coil. After winding is completed, the wire coils tend to spring outward slightly, which results in a finished product that is slightly larger than the form. This springing action makes it easy to remove the form from the center of the coil.

Hold the form in your left hand (reverse these directions if you are lefthanded) and place the front end of the coil wire between your thumb and the form while pressing firmly. Now, begin winding the wire around the form (Fig. 3-4). Each turn of wire should be wound so that it is touching the previous turn for the entire circumference. When the required number of turns have been wound, wind a few more. You can always cut a coil with too many turns down to size, but adding turns to a coil that lacks a few is next to impossible.

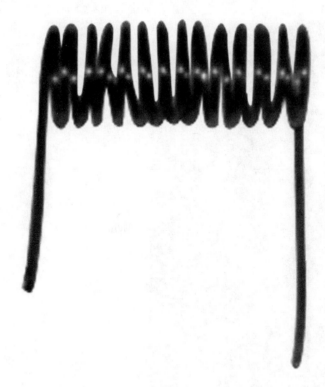

3-4
A loading coil.

At this point, remove your thumb from the front end of the wire and gently slide the coil off the form. Proper spacing of each of the close wound turns can then be achieved by running a small circular object (such as a pencil) through the turns by starting at the front and continuing between the turns until it slips out of the other end. Measure the spacing and if too little separation has been achieved, try a larger object and run it through again until the proper dimensions are achieved. Spacing that is too wide can be easily rectified by slipping the coil back on to the original winding form and twisting it with both hands moving in opposite directions while pulling the turns closer together (Fig. 3-5). After you have done this, you need to begin spacing all over again.

The coil will be more efficient if even spacing is maintained throughout. Take care not to mash any of the circular turns. The first turn of most coils should be identical to the last and spaced the same distance from the next closest turn. Coils of the variety just described are called *self-supporting*. They require no support because the stiffness of the wire used provides adequate rigidity. Normally, #12 or #14 bare copper wire is used and it does a good job on coils with a few turns.

Larger coils or coils with many turns of wire present too great a support problem for this size wire or any other practical size. For these large coils, a different type of mechanical rigidity is required. This rigidity is achieved by the use of epoxy cement. Wind the coil in the same way, but firmly anchor the front of the wire with electrical tape before starting the winding procedure. When the coil is spaced and

3-5
Tightening a coil.

completed, anchor the opposite end in the same manner. Now apply epoxy cement across the turns of the entire coil in strips on four sides. Make certain that the cement does not come in contact with the form, only with the turns of the coil. Allow adequate time for the epoxy cement to dry, then remove your completed coil for mounting in your antenna system. For outdoor mounting, small coils can be completely encased in epoxy with only the two ends protruding for connections. Carefully check a coil prepared in this manner to make certain it has the correct number of turns and proper spacing for your project, because once it's encased in the epoxy you can't turn back. A mistake at this point requires the construction of a new coil.

Wiring cable connectors

Many shortwave receivers provide a connector on the back for a secure antenna connection to the set. This connector is usually the type that matches a common male connector, known as a PL-259. The correct connector wiring can be accomplished in five steps, as shown in Fig. 3-6.

1. Using RG-58 coaxial cable, remove the black outside jacket insulation for 3″ (Figs. 3-6A and 3-6B), and be very careful not to cut the braided conductor.

Remember to slide the collar of the connector and any adapters down the coaxial cable. I have soldered connectors onto coaxial cable only to find that I had forgotten to put the collar on the coax first. That left me with no alternative but to unsolder the joints, remove the PL-259, and start over.

2. Unbraid down one side of the braided outer conductor (Fig. 3-6C). Pull the braid together into one strand, twist it together (Fig. 3-6D), and carefully draw it through the hole in the inner sleeve of the PL-259. Then, solder the braid to the sleeve. Or, instead of pulling the braid back, leave it on and cut it at the same place that you cut the inner dielectric insulation. Then, solder the braid solid. The PL-259 will then slide over the end of the coaxial cable and the outside will make contact with the braided shield.

3. Bare one-half of the center conductor by carefully stripping away the white center dielectric just under the braid (Fig. 3-6E). Be careful not to nick the center conductor.

4. Push the plug assembly onto the cable and make sure that the center conductor slides easily into the hollow tip (Fig. 3-6F). Screw the plug to the outside plug shield and solder the braid through the holes that are located at the halfway point on the plug assembly (Fig. 3-6G). Solder the center conductor to the hollow sleeve tip (Fig. 3-6H), and be certain not to drop any loose solder on the outside. If the center conductor is longer than the hollow tip, cut the excess off.

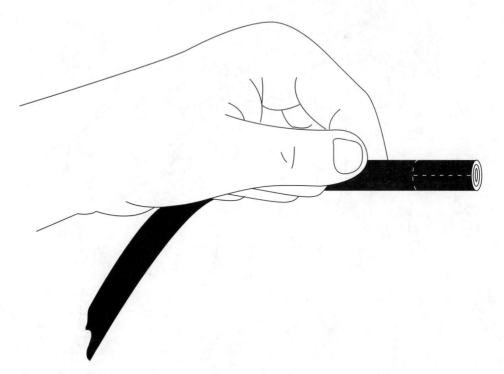

3-6A Preparing the coaxial cable and adding a standard PL-259 connector to the end of the transmission line of an antenna. Cut along dotted lines with a knife.

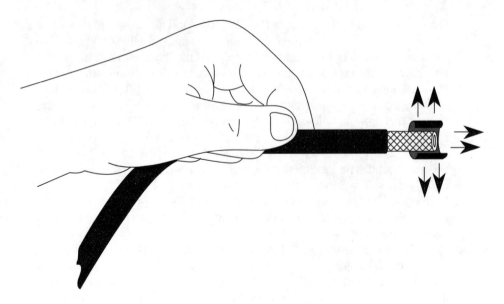

3-6B Remove outer jacket.

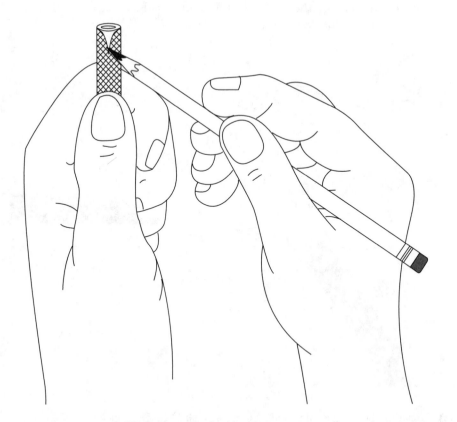

3-6C Separate the braid with a pen or pencil.

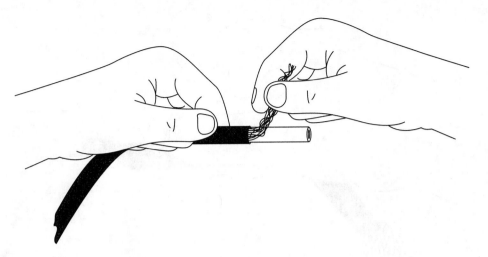

3-6D Twist the braid into one thick "wire."

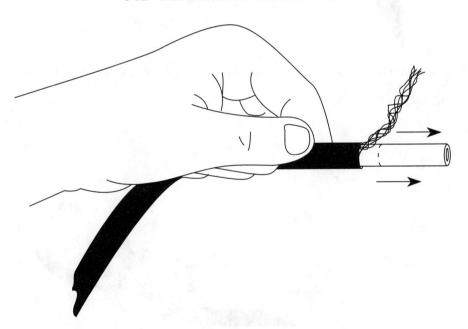

3-6E Carefully cut and remove the dielectric.

5. Screw the collar to the plug assembly. The wiring is complete. Figure 3-7 shows a PL-259 being plugged into an SO-239.

One point of contention is the type of coaxial cable used. Like some antenna builders, I prefer the larger RG-8U coaxial cable for better signal strength over long transmission line runs. If you go with smaller cable, you need to use a UG-175 or UG-176 adapter to match the size of the cable. The wiring process is then followed exactly as for the RG-58 cable.

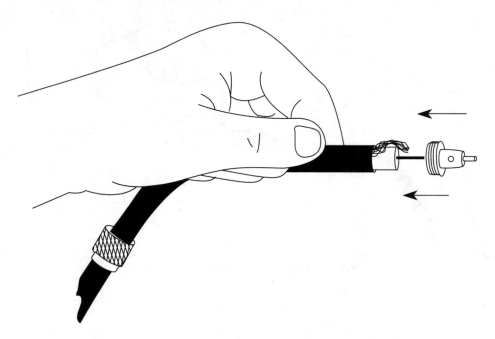

3-6F Slide the PL-259 sleeve down the coax, then slide the end of the PL-259 onto the end of the coax.

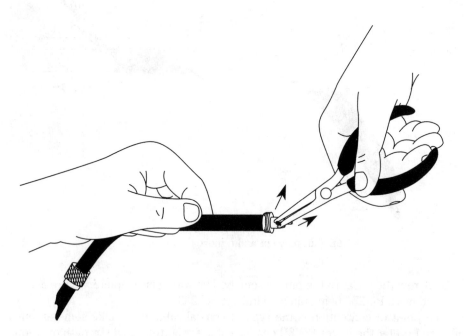

3-6G Pull the end of the braid through the hole in the side of the PL-259 end.

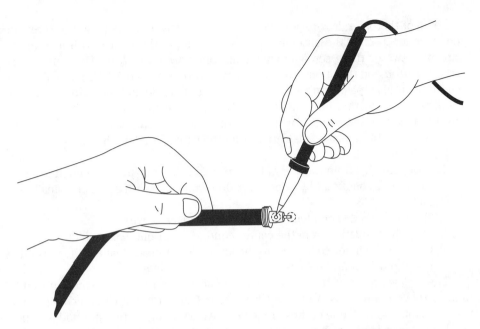

3-6H Solder thoroughly at the two points circled in the illustration.

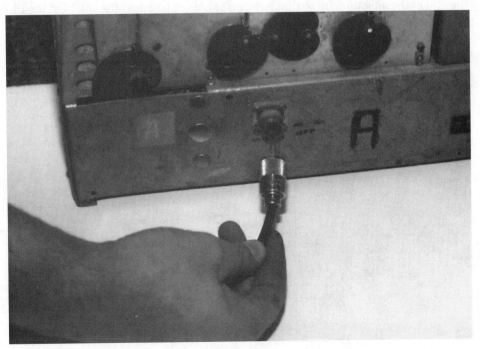

3-7 A PL-259 being plugged into an SO-239 connector.

Some of the older, less-expensive shortwave receivers do not use the screw-in type of connector for the antenna but instead supply the owner with a terminal board with two or three screw connections called *terminal lugs*. One terminal is marked *ground* and the others are marked *antenna* or A1 and A2. Coaxial cable can be used with this type of connector by separating the braid and the outer connector into distinct conductors for connection to the back of the receiver. The following steps produce the best results for this type of cable preparation:

1. Strip the black plastic insulation from the cable for a length of 2". Do not nick the braid.
2. To a point 1¾" from the end of the stripped cable, separate the braid from the center conductor by unbraiding down one side with a pen or a small nail.
3. Twist the braided conductor into one thick piece of wire.
4. Strip the insulation from the center conductor for one-half inch only.
5. Connect the inner conductor to the antenna terminal. Connect the twisted braid to the ground terminal. The wiring is complete.

These days, most of the less-expensive shortwave radios are small, portable units with whip antennas. You might want to use an antenna with a coaxial cable transmission line with one of these receivers. An easy connection method is to use an alligator clip lead (such as the type used in chapter 1). Connect one alligator clip to the center conductor of the PL-259 and pull the rubber clip insulator over the end of the alligator clip so that it doesn't short out against the shield of the PL-259. Then, attach the other alligator clip to the whip antenna of the portable receiver (Fig. 3-8).

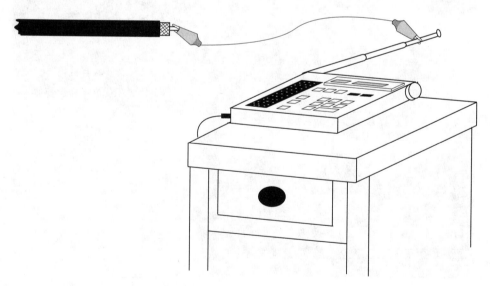

3-8 Using a set of test leads to connect a PL-259 to a portable receiver.

Running transmission line inside

Many shortwave listeners spend hours improving the height of the antenna above ground, obtaining strong solder joints, protecting the transmission line against damage and so on. One of the last points of consideration for most short-wave listeners is how the transmission line or antenna feeds from the outdoors to your receiver.

With very basic wire antennas, it's common to simply run the wire out at the bottom of the windowsill, and then close the window on it. If you close a window on coaxial cable, you will damage the cable and/or allow plenty of cold air or insects into your home. One simple method is to drill a hole through the window frame or sill so that the coaxial cable fits through the hole (Fig. 3-9). Then, use outdoor-quality caulking to seal the inside and the outside holes. My dad used this method on my bedroom window when I was a teenager and it worked well.

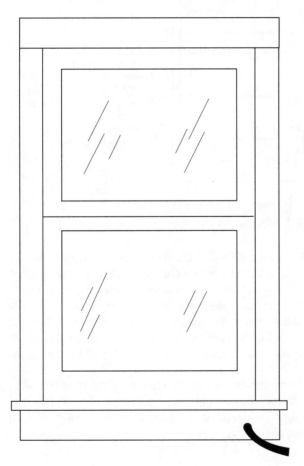

3-9
A section of coaxial cable running through a hole in the windowsill.

A more sophisticated method of coaxial cable entry is to cut a small panel out of the outside wall of the house (Fig. 3-10). Of course, you must be sure that no hot electrical wires, pipes, or other dangerous obstacles lie in your path. Next, cut panels to fit over the outside of both sides of the hole. Then, drill a hole in the outside panel so that a panel-mounted SO-239 connector can be screwed into the panel. Drill a hole that is the same diameter as the coaxial cable in the inside panel. Afterwards, cut a short piece of coaxial cable so that it reaches from the hole in the wall to the radio. The coaxial cable should then be soldered (following previous directions) to the SO-239 in the outside panel. Mount the outside panel on the outside of the house with screws, fill the hole with insulation, run the coaxial cable through the holes in the inside panel, and mount that panel over the hole on the inside. Caulk around the edges of the panel and put a PL-259 (following previous directions) on the end of the cable.

3-10
A panel in the side of the house that contains SO-239 connectors soldered together on either side so that new antennas or receivers can easily be connected together.

I haven't lived in a house for a long enough period of time to consider cutting holes in the outside walls. If you would like to try a technique with somewhat similar results, except that you don't have to cut holes in the outside of the house, try building a connector panel (almost like the last hole-in-the-wall project) that fits exactly in the window (Fig. 3-11). If you use two panels that are sealed together with small strips of wood (forming a tight box), fill the inside with insulation, and place weather stripping around the outside edges, your antenna connection box will be energy efficient.

The last method of protecting your coaxial cable while keeping your house as airtight as possible is the quick'n'dirty window method. Cut a piece of wood (such as a 2×4) to the width of the window. Then, cut or drill a groove across one side. Run the cable through this groove and out the window.

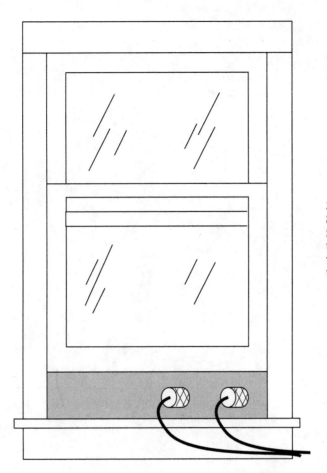

3-11
Several SO-239 connectors
installed in a 2 × 4 to direct
transmission line outside
without cutting any holes in
the house.

4
CHAPTER

Types of shortwave listening antennas

Antennas come in many different shapes, sizes, and configurations, but even the most complex antennas consist of the basic vertical or horizontal designs, or a combination of both. This chapter covers the general types of antennas, and their advantages and disadvantages. It provides you with the necessary information to make your final choice of an antenna system to suit your individual needs.

Vertical antenna configurations

The term *vertical antenna* encompasses a large group of antenna systems that are designed for mobile, portable, and fixed base operations. Some vertical antennas are mounted at ground level, using the earth ground below them to act as the negative side of the antenna. Figure 4-1 shows various vertical antenna designs. Figure 4-1A shows a basic vertical antenna with a ground system composed of uninsulated copper wire buried several inches below the soil. The vertical portion of this antenna is not connected to the portion below the earth, but is connected at the end just above ground level to the antenna input of the SWL receiver. The chassis or ground coupling is connected to the buried copper wires. Figure 4-1B shows a vertical antenna known as a *ground plane*. This antenna is similar to the one shown in Fig. 4-1A, but it is mounted a distance above earth level. The ground plane antenna uses an artificial ground system—three sections of aluminum tubing that extend diagonally from the bottom end of the vertical portion. This antenna has the advantage of being mounted higher above ground level, while still providing an adequate grounding system. Each section of tubing or radial of the artificial ground is the same length as the vertical tube or *radiator*. The antennas shown in Figs. 4-1A and 4-1B are most often called *quarter-wave verticals*.

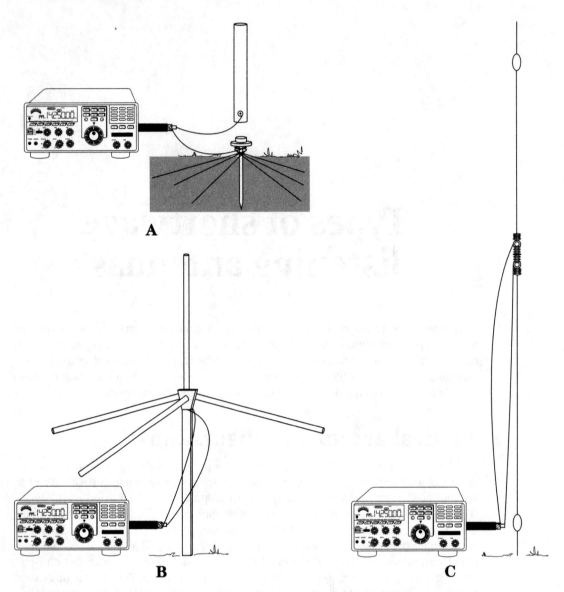

4-1 Several types of vertical antennas: A) the quarter-wavelength vertical, B) the ground plane, and C) the vertical dipole.

Figure 4-1C shows a different type of vertical antenna, the vertical half-wave dipole. It is twice as tall as its quarter-wave counterparts and a separate ground system is not required. This antenna can be fed to the receiver at its center; the lower portion acts as the ground and the upper portion serves as the radiator.

Because radio signals travel at the speed of light, a wavelength is a measurement of how far a radio signal travels during one cycle of its transmission. The distance differs for various frequencies, so antenna lengths and heights are different. A frequency of 3 MHz (three million cycles per second) completes one cycle in ⅓,₀₀₀,₀₀₀ of a second. During the duration of that cycle, the radio wave travels 100 meters, therefore one wavelength at 3 MHz is 100 meters. One quarter wavelength is one quarter of that distance, or 25 meters. A quarter wavelength antenna for 3 MHz then would be 25 meters long or roughly 67'. A simple formula is provided later to enable you to easily figure antenna length in feet and inches for any given operating frequency.

Every antenna has its individual advantages and disadvantages. The quarter-wave vertical is easy to set up. It is mounted in close proximity to the earth, which allows the feed line to the receiver to run along or be buried under the surface. A disadvantage of this antenna comes to light when large objects surround the antenna site. The radiator portion of the quarter-wave vertical antenna might not be high enough to clear these obstacles, resulting in poor signal reception from certain directions. The quarter-wave ground plane can be mounted as high above the earth's surface as is practical because it carries its own artificial ground system (Fig. 4-1B). Small ceramic insulators are used at a point in the wire where the correct length is attained. This antenna system has the disadvantage of requiring a wooden or aluminum support for the radial extension. The half-wave vertical requires no additional grounding system. The entire antenna is in the vertical plane (no horizontal ground wires) and usually it has enough height with the radiator portion to clear common surrounding objects. There are disadvantages: The radiator must be supported by a nonmetallic mast (such as a wooden pole), and the feed line to the SWL receiver should be brought straight away from the center of the antenna for several feet at a 90° angle (Fig. 4-1C).

If you decide on a vertical antenna configuration for your site, the location of your receiver might help you decide which type to build. If the receiver is located on the ground floor, perhaps the quarter-wave antenna will serve best, because the feed line is connected to the antenna at ground level and can be run along the soil surface to the receiver, which is on about the same level. This would decrease the length of transmission line, which saves you a few dollars and increases the received signal strength. There is always a small loss in signal strength during the journey along the transmission line to the receiver. The shorter the feed line, the lower the signal loss. This signal strength loss in the transmission line is called *attenuation*.

If your radio is located in a second-story room, perhaps the half-wave antenna would be the better choice. The transmission line departs from the antenna at a point higher above the ground and closer to the height of many second-story buildings. Again, the transmission line length can be kept to the absolute minimum, and for the same reason a ground plane antenna might be ideal for the lucky shortwave listener who has requisitioned an attic or top-story operating area. The ground plane can be mounted a few feet above the roof or chimney, and a short length of cable can be extended along the side of the building and into the receiver location. These are only some of the reasons for selecting a certain type of vertical antenna. Cost might dictate your final decision, and the quarter-wave vertical usually wins every time—especially if an overhanging branch from a tall tree is close by to provide a means of supporting the radiating element (Fig. 4-1B). This type of vertical antenna usually provides the least expensive and least complicated installation.

If vertical space is limited, there are several ways to shorten an antenna while still providing acceptable reception. The installation of a loading coil (Fig. 4-2) at the base, center, or top of the radiating element allows a considerable reduction in physical height, while still obtaining an antenna that is electrically equivalent to a full-sized version. The loading coil causes the antenna to perform electrically at the desired frequencies. That is, it "convinces" the incoming signal that the antenna is full size. Generally, the higher the loading coil is placed in the vertical element, the better the reception. Loading coils do an excellent job of increasing the electrical length of vertical antennas, but a full-size antenna provides superior performance. Do not consider a less than full-sized antenna system unless absolutely necessary. Coils are sometimes used in conjunction with variable capacitors to match transmission lines to shortwave listening receivers that are designed to accept inputs at a different impedance than the one the antenna or transmission line provides. These should not be confused with loading coils.

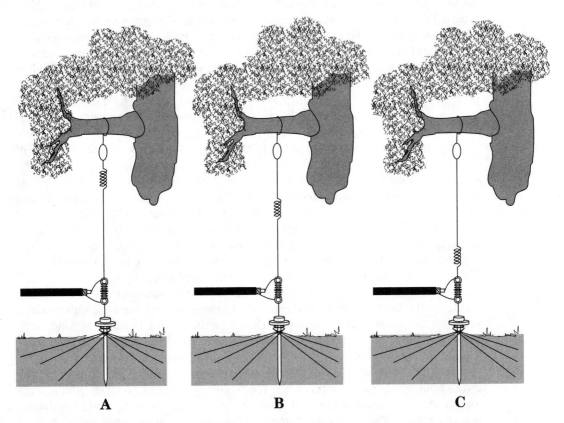

A   **B**   **C**

4-2 Various methods of coil-loading vertical antennas: A) top loaded, B) center loaded, and C) bottom loaded.

Loading coils appear only between the transmission line and the antenna or in the antenna itself. Impedance is the combination of resistance and other electrical factors in the transmission line. Many SWL receivers are designed to operate into a feed line of about 50-ohm (Ω) impedance. When the impedance of the antenna and line is appreciably different, coils and capacitors are sometimes used to bring the impedance up, or down, to a level the receiver can accept and use properly. All antenna projects contained in the later chapters are designed to operate at the impedance level of most modern shortwave receivers, which is normally 50 to 75 Ω.

As mentioned earlier, the vertical element of each antenna system should be as close to vertical as possible. In some cases, this is impossible and a severe departure from absolute vertical is necessary. This type of antenna (Fig. 4-3) is sometimes known as a *slant antenna* or *slant vertical*. In most instances, this particular type of antenna arrangement is convenient for the quarter-wave vertical only and provides good reception if it is designed properly. The slant antenna requires more horizontal site space, but it is most suited to a location where the top of the antenna must be connected to a support that is not directly above the preferred transmission line feed point. It is not a true vertical antenna, but it exhibits many of the traits and properties of the basic vertical configuration and is usually fed to the receiver by standard methods. Figure 4-4 provides examples of various vertical antenna systems and shows a sampling of standard and unorthodox vertical element arrangements.

Horizontal antenna configurations

Horizontal antenna systems are constructed of a single length of wire mounted horizontally to the earth. The most common horizontal antenna is the dipole, which is normally a half-wavelength long. Dipole antennas are usually fed from the center of the wire or element to the receiver with a single wire, a length of TV twin-lead, or coaxial cable. Some dipole antennas are constructed of several lengths of wire that are spaced an equal distance from the center element for broader frequency coverage. Figure 4-5 shows examples of several common dipole antenna configurations.

A dipole antenna is one of the easiest antenna systems to construct, and it can be erected in a short period of time if the wire lengths are cut to size and insulators are installed while on the ground. The entire system can then be hoisted to its permanent mounting position, and you can begin listening. Two supports, spaced considerable distances from each other, must be available in order to mount the dipole antenna. The transmission line to the receiver is then brought down from the center and into the radio room.

Unlike the vertical antenna, which tends to receive signals from all directions, the dipole antenna is most efficient at receiving signals that are on a line that intersects either side of the main element. Signals that strike this antenna at either end are received weakly or not at all. The dipole tends to be a bidirectional antenna, receiving signals from two directions, while disregarding signals coming from other directions. Some shortwave listeners use two perpendicular dipoles. That way, the shortwave listener has the option of switching between antennas for the best signal.

To achieve the standard reception patterns of the horizontal dipole, it should be mounted as closely as possible to a true horizontal position. As with all antennas, slight variations are acceptable, but the reception patterns change as the horizontal position is varied. The inverted-V antenna is an example of a large variation in a horizontal antenna system. Figure 4-6 shows the inverted-V in its standard configura-

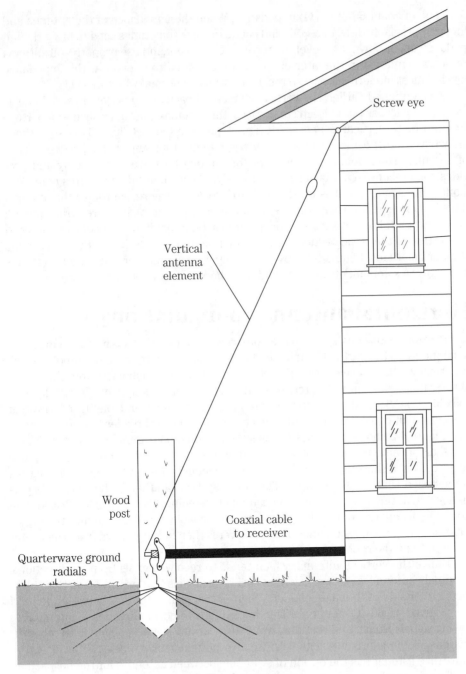

Screw eye

Vertical
antenna
element

Wood
post

Coaxial cable
to receiver

Quarterwave ground
radials

4-3 The slant antenna.

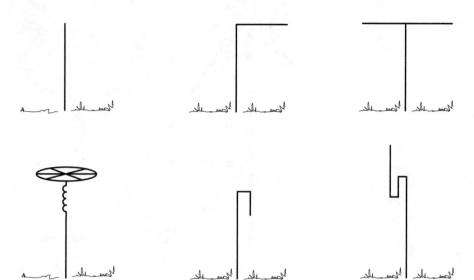

4-4 Various vertical antenna element configurations.

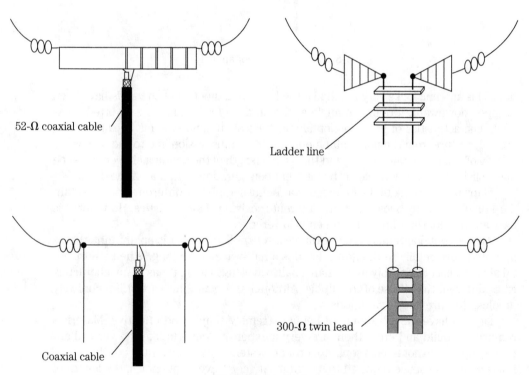

4-5 Different dipole antennas.

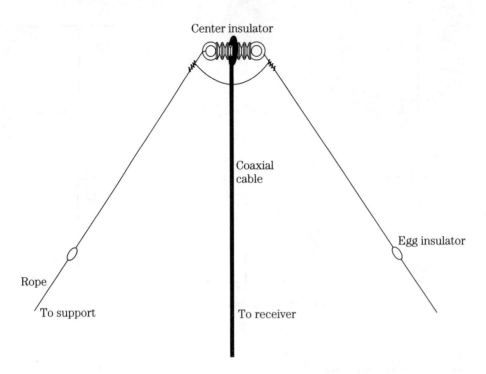

Center insulator

Coaxial
cable

Egg insulator

Rope

To support

To receiver

4-6 The inverted-V antenna.

tion. This antenna looks very much like the horizontal dipole, but the ends have been dropped downward, forming an angle at the antenna feed point. The inverted-V exhibits characteristics of both horizontal and vertical antenna systems because of the great departure from the horizontal mounting. The transmission line to the receiver is usually of a different impedance, and the overall length of the antenna element must be made slightly shorter because of the different configuration from that of the dipole.

Many people think of the inverted-V as being completely different from the standard dipole—mostly because of the different receiving characteristics. However, it is basically a dipole antenna with the ends lowered.

All horizontal antennas are not dipoles. A *dipole antenna* is an antenna that is mounted horizontally to the ground and is a half-wavelength long. When a horizontal antenna is considerably more than a half-wavelength long, it has many characteristics different than those of the dipole. Although these antennas are still technically dipoles, they are longer variations.

Dipoles have the advantage of being extremely simple and effective. Materials required to build and erect them are very inexpensive, and, unlike the vertical antenna, dipoles do not need a separate ground system. One disadvantage of the dipole is the amount of space required to mount it. At shortwave frequencies, the length of half-wave dipole ranges from approximately 180' to 15' long. For some people, the lower-frequency dipoles are out of the question, but for those with some real estate, it is a viable option. As with most antennas, you can make considerable changes from the textbook versions and still have a good-performing antenna. You can squeeze a 180' dipole into a 130' space, but the antenna will not operate as a true dipole. Fig-

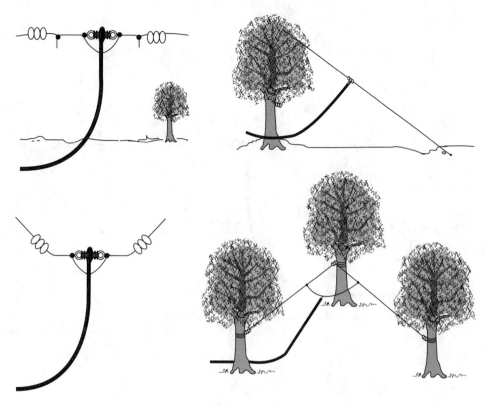

4-7 Horizontal dipoles.

ure 4-7 shows some horizontal dipoles in other than completely horizontal configurations. When building an antenna like these, you might need to improvise considerably to obtain a performance that you find to be acceptable.

It is extremely difficult for one antenna to perform efficiently at all frequencies covered by the shortwave frequency spectrum. The ideal system would have several different antennas that were designed for several different parts of the shortwave band. The fan dipole has a very good chance of fulfilling this requirement while eliminating the need for many different feed lines to the receiver. Figure 4-8 shows a fan dipole antenna system that is made of three different antennas all connected to the same point at the center. This antenna is fed to the receiver by one length of coaxial cable. Each of the three elements is designed for a different portion of the shortwave band. This antenna system covers much of the entire band, uses one transmission line, and requires only slightly more space than a standard dipole antenna if each antenna element is mounted slightly below the other.

Other multiband antennas could include a system that is made up of both horizontal and vertical elements, as pictured in Fig. 4-9. One horizontal element and one vertical element are shown, but several of each type of element could be used where practicality and space availability permit. It is nearly impossible to include all of the various horizontal antenna variations that a shortwave listener is likely to run across during years of involvement in this hobby.

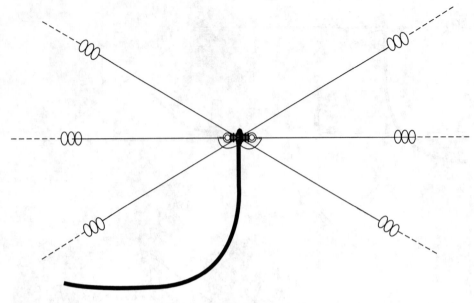

4-8 A fan dipole antenna system.

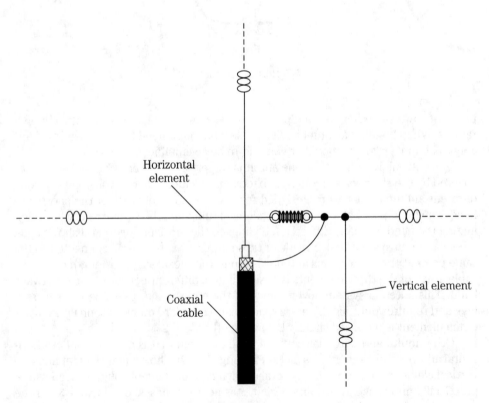

Horizontal element

Coaxial cable

Vertical element

4-9 A multiband antenna.

Directional antenna systems

The last type of antenna system covered in this chapter is best understood after learning about the basic vertical and horizontal antennas. Directional antenna systems are composed of parts of each of these basic antennas, and sometimes of both. A directional antenna receives radio signals arriving at the antenna from one specific direction and disregards signals that arrive from other directions. The directional antenna has the advantage of providing more sensitive reception from its main coverage direction while cutting down on static, noise, and radio interference from directions of no immediate interest to the particular shortwave listener. Earlier, I stated that the common dipole antenna is *bidirectional*, receiving signals equally well from two opposite directions. A directional antenna is usually thought of as being *unidirectional*, receiving well from one direction only.

A minimum of two elements are required to have a true directional antenna. The main or radiating element is the same length or height as the basic antenna elements described earlier and is connected to the shortwave receiver. The second element is called either a *director* or *reflector,* depending on which is utilized. Figure 4-10 shows the basic two-element horizontal antenna. Notice that the director system (Fig. 4-10A) uses the second element in front of the main element. In other words, the incoming signal intercepts the director first and then the main receiving element. The reflector system (Fig. 4-10B) is just the opposite in that it is mounted behind the main element (in relationship to the incoming signal). An easy way to think of each element's performance in the system is to picture the director as pulling the signal into the main element, and the reflector as bouncing the signal back into the main element. Although

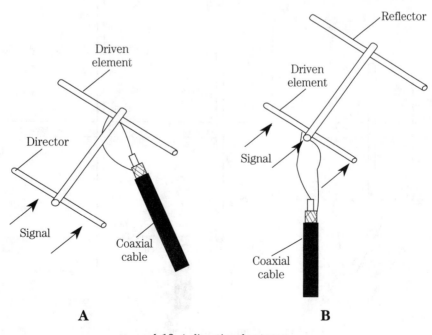

4-10 A directional antenna.

not a completely accurate technical explanation of how the antenna operates, it is an easy way to think of what the antenna does with the incoming signal.

Some antenna systems use a reflector, a main or driven element, and a director. In some cases, many directors are used (as in a standard TV antenna), but usually only one reflector is utilized in a system—no matter what the size. Each element that is added provides more gain as a whole. The main element is almost identical with a basic one-element antenna. The reflector is longer by 7% and the director is shorter by a like percentage. If more than one director is used, the element lengths grow even shorter so that the director farthest from the main element is the shortest element in the system and the element lengths continue to increase through the main element and to the reflector. If more than one reflector is used, the length of the second reflector would be longer than the first and so on.

Figure 4-11 shows a multielement horizontal directional antenna system, or beam. You'll see that the signal enters at the narrow end of the antenna and travels to the main element and reflector. Signals striking this antenna from the sides are not received (or at least not very strongly) and the same is true of signals that approach this system from the back, or reflector, side.

Directional antenna systems require precisely measured element lengths. The antenna wire must be measured to within a fraction of an inch. The spacing between each element is also critical. A system comprised of more than two elements is often as long as it is wide. Much additional space is required, making multielement directional antenna systems impractical for all but the shortwave frequencies above about 13 MHz.

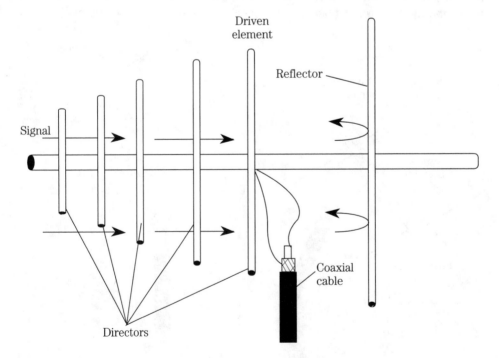

4-11 A multielement directional antenna.

Directional wire antennas

As stated earlier, directional antenna systems almost always require more than one antenna element. As always, there is an exception—the longwire antenna (Fig. 4-12). Longwire antennas are exactly what the name implies—long wires. A single wire that is several wavelengths long at the operating frequency is directional from either end, unlike the common dipole antenna, which receives broadside to the antenna wire. This type of antenna is ideal for shortwave listeners on farms and in rural areas, where up to several thousand feet of antenna space are available. This antenna is the only practical directional system that serves on the lower shortwave frequencies (if it can be placed high enough in the air). Longwire directional antennas can even be rotated to change receiving directions if two distant anchoring points are available at the mounting site (Fig. 4-13).

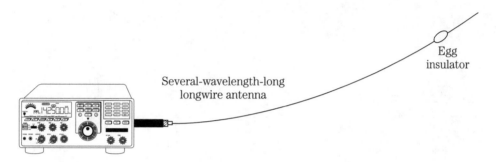

4-12 A longwire antenna.

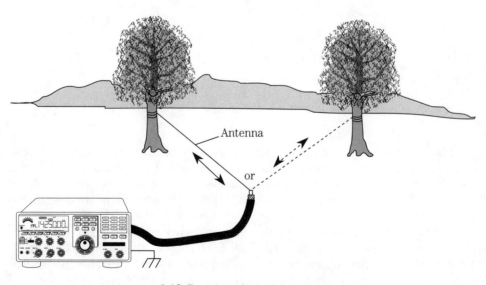

4-13 Rotating a longwire antenna.

There are many variations on this directional antenna design, including systems with two or more elements. One of these is the V, which is shown in Fig. 4-14. Each element of the V is at least several times as long as each element in the inverted-V antenna for the same frequency. Depending on the length of the two elements in the V antenna, the angle between the two ranges from 90° to about 40°.

The longer the element length, the smaller the angle. The smallest V for a specific shortwave frequency is twice as sensitive as a standard dipole antenna at the same frequency, but each element of the smallest V (down to about 30°) is twice the length of the entire dipole antenna.

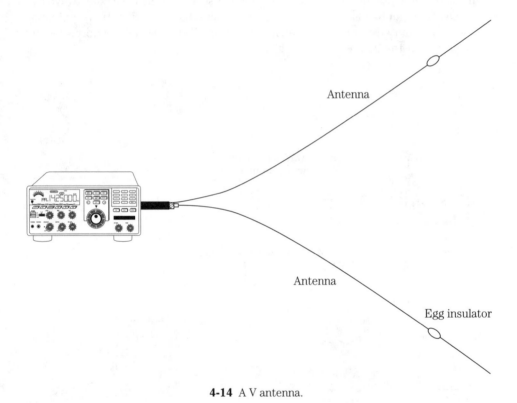

4-14 A V antenna.

The rhombic antenna shown in Fig. 4-15 is a combination of longwire antenna systems. It can be used over a large number of shortwave frequencies and exhibits a considerable amount of gain over a dipole antenna. Gain is the measurement of antenna sensitivity over a reference antenna. This antenna requires a tremendous amount of space and is not practical for many shortwave listeners.

The only high cost involved with the rhombic design would be in purchasing the four supports for the corners of the rhombic. Each support should be a minimum of 50' in height, with the spacing between a minimum of 300'. This antenna can be made infinitely larger with a continued increase in antenna gain and sensitivity.

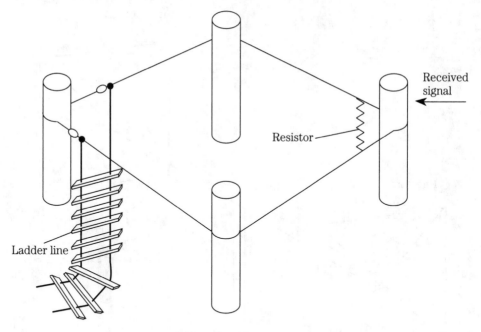

4-15 A rhombic antenna.

Cubical quads

If you are short on space, but want the advantages gained from a directional antenna system, all is not lost. The cubical quad antenna shown in Fig. 4-16 might be the answer to your problems. This cubical quad uses two elements, each of which is a type of single-element loop antenna. One element is the reflector, which is slightly longer than one wavelength at the operating frequency. The other element is the main receiving element, which is closer to an exact wavelength.

Each wire element is formed into a square, which is supported at the corners by bamboo or fiberglass poles. The two elements are mechanically joined by a length of aluminum tubing (or boom), which is cut to provide the calculated spacing required. This extremely lightweight directional antenna system can easily be lifted. The cubical quad antenna requires half of the horizontal mounting space of a basic dipole antenna for the same frequency. Each of the four sides of the individual elements are approximately one-quarter wavelength in size. Practical limitations generally keep the cubical quad antenna restricted to the frequencies above 13 MHz. Its light weight has the advantage of making it easy to turn in different directions by using an ordinary television antenna rotator. A properly built two-element cubical quad usually performs as well as a three-element horizontal directional, plus the vertical portion of the quad extends higher above ground than the horizontal beam if it is mounted on the same support.

The cubical quad can also be constructed to cover a wide range of shortwave bands with no increase in its overall size. Figure 4-17 shows a cubical quad that is

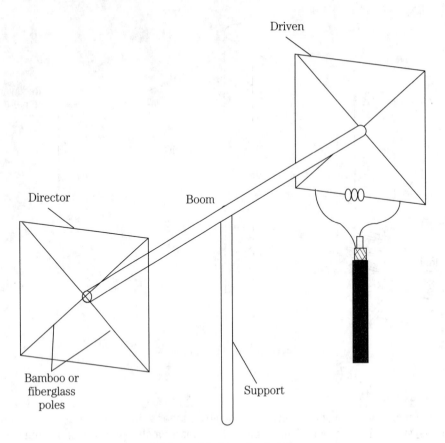

4-16 A cubical quad antenna.

designed to cover three specific frequency ranges. The low-frequency element is the longest and is positioned on the outside edge of the pole spacers. The second element is designed for a slightly higher frequency. Thus, it requires less antenna wire length and it can be mounted inside of the first element on the same spacers. The third element is for an even higher frequency and it is the smallest. All three elements can usually be connected to the same feed line, which is normally a length of coaxial cable that runs directly to the shortwave receiver. The reflector elements in the cubical quad are designed and spaced in the same manner. Again, cubical quad antennas are generally restricted to the frequencies above 13 MHz because of sheer size, but a few have been constructed for frequencies as low as 7 MHz and at least one was designed and erected to cover the 3-MHz band. At this low frequency, each side of the element was approximately 67' long. The main disadvantage of the cubical quad antenna is its appearance. It might be efficient and lightweight, but it looks like a behemoth when placed in its final operating position. Figure 4-18 shows different mounting angles that can be applied to the cubical quad. Personal tastes and practicality might influence your decision on which configuration appeals most to you.

1st,
2nd, and
3rd elements

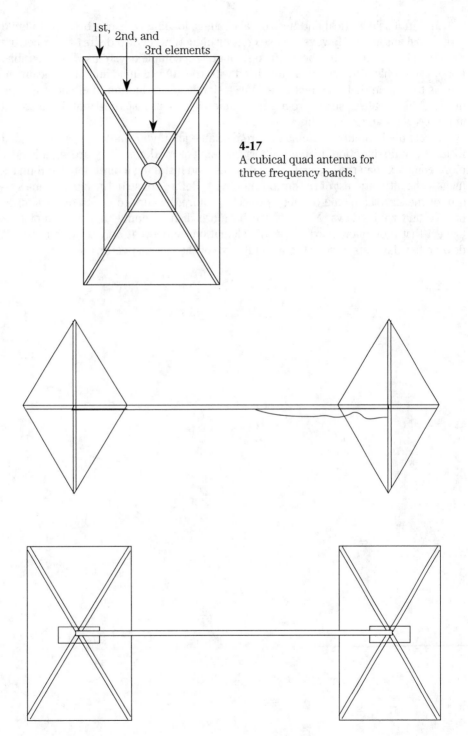

4-17
A cubical quad antenna for
three frequency bands.

4-18 Mounting positions for cubical quads. The upper quad is vertically polarized
and the lower is horizontally polarized.

As with basic vertical and horizontal designs, loading coils can be used to build directional antennas. However, these coils or inductors tend to distort the receiving directional pattern and are best left to smaller, less complex systems when possible. Loading coils have been successfully used with the cubical quad and other beam antennas to reduce their element sizes, but a significant reduction in element length, in most cases, causes so severe a performance loss that basic horizontal or vertical antennas work almost as well.

Directional antenna systems do a remarkable job if you want to receive a signal from a specific direction, instead of just listening at random. They are significantly more complex than the basic antenna designs, and installing a directional antenna is usually the ultimate test of the serious hobbyist. Before constructing an antenna system of the size that some of these projects require, be sure to check on local ordinances and zoning laws. Nothing can be more disheartening than to complete a project that took many hard weeks of calculations and sweat only to have to tear it down a few days later under the watchful eye of the city inspector.

5
CHAPTER

Masts and supports

Once you have constructed an antenna, the next dilemma is how to get it into the air. Very few antennas are effective on the ground. If you are lucky and have some land around your house (assuming that you live in a house and not in an apartment building), you might be able to attach the antenna to a tree or building. This eliminates the need to purchase a tower or other supporting device, and saves you quite a bit of money and time.

Safety

The first word of masts and towers is *safety*. That's it. If you die or get sued out of your house because of a faulty mast, your antenna won't do you much good. Make sure that your antenna mast is soundly designed by following good engineering practices, and that you follow local ordinances regarding antenna installation.

The primary safety concern for your antenna is that it must not be within falling distance of power lines. For example, don't even think of putting a 35' tower within 35' of power lines. In fact, it should be at least a few feet further away, in case your estimated distance is incorrect or if something bizarre happens (such as if a hurricane blows your mast over).

Also be careful that you do not raise a mast or tower anywhere near power lines. Every year, stories abound about amateur radio operators who are electrocuted accidently when they touch power lines while raising a mast or tower. It doesn't matter if you are using a metal mast or something supposedly nonconductive, such as PVC or wood, power lines are still extremely dangerous and should most certainly be avoided.

Before building an antenna or even working on plans for a mast, call the local authorities. In most cases, you can call either the city or borough manager or an inspector who is employed by the township that you live in. That person can tell you what types of antenna towers are permissible where you live. Ordinances vary from town to town, so get complete, verified information. Some historic towns don't allow outdoor antennas of any sort, so it is up to you to find out.

Last, this book is merely a guide to installing your own antennas. Conditions vary around the country and not every antenna mast is safe in every location. Thus, it is your responsibility to make sure that your antennas and antenna masts are strategically placed and structurally sound. In fact, it is a good idea to ask the local building inspector or another engineer who is certified to authorize antennas to look at your plans, offer suggestions as to how the plans can be improved, and inspect the final product.

Supporting antennas in trees and on buildings

Securing the end of an antenna element to a rigid structure, such as a building, is a simple matter. Although I have driven a small nail into a window frame of our house in the past to attach temporary antennas, it's not the best, or safest, solution. When running wire antennas alongside houses or other buildings, it is safer to use stand-off insulators or insulated screw eyes, in case of a lightning strike. For the same reason, you should use rope, not wire or metal cable, to support antennas (at the ends of dipoles, for example). Because of durability and weather resistance, nylon cord or rope is an excellent choice for supporting wire antennas. It's easy to attach wire antennas (via their support ropes) to towers, posts, poles, etc. Just securely knot the rope around the structure.

Over the years, I have probably used hundreds of trees to hang antennas in or to tie off antenna support ropes. Some antenna texts advise against securing wire antennas to trees. The theory is that when trees sway in the wind, they can snap either the wire antenna or the securing rope. This theory sounds reasonable, but I almost always secure my antennas in trees, and I have never had any problems with antennas breaking under the stress of high winds (although one or two have been taken out by ice storms). I suppose that if I ever want an antenna to stay airborne for a substantial period of time (a decade or so), I will guard against the sway from trees.

One simple measure to keep your antennas off the ground is to use stranded wire. Unlike stranded wire, solid wire is unable to resist the constant flexing that is important for an outdoor antenna. Another important point is to keep stress off of the antenna. A device is needed to take up slack in the antenna system during no-wind conditions, but it must allow adequate "play" in the antenna when the wind blows. The common pulley does the job simply and efficiently. Figure 5-1 shows such an arrangement. The pulley is secured to the tree with a length of nylon rope. One end of the antenna element is secured to a different rope that is run through the pulley and then down toward the ground for several feet. A sizable weight is connected to the end of the rope nearest the ground. You'll need to experiment with the amount of weight for your antenna system. The length of the antenna, the wind-sway resistance of the tree, and other factors dictate the amount to use. The correct value is not critical or especially difficult to calculate.

Don't forget that tree trunks are alive and are somewhat pliable. These points are especially apparent if you have spent much time in farming areas and have seen

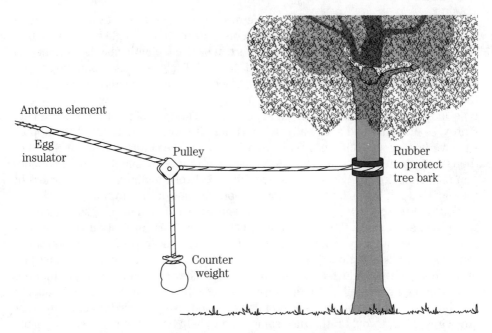

5-1 Using a pulley to mount the end of an antenna in a tree.

trees that have totally enveloped barbed-wire fences over the years. The point here isn't so much that trees might envelope your antenna like the Blob, but that outer tree layers consist of flexible, living "skin." If you are careless with your antenna installation, you could damage or kill a beautiful old tree. The tree must be protected from the possibility of being cut by the rope length that secures the pulley. Several small pieces of wood or a piece of rubber from a tire secured to the tree between the branch and the wire should be adequate.

By examining Fig. 5-1, you can see that when the tree sways in the wind, the pulley-rope combination automatically adjusts the slack as conditions require. In order to keep the system working properly, you should check it occasionally to make sure that the rope isn't tangled and that nothing is lodged in the pulley. If the rope begins to fray, replace it immediately. The last thing you want is the pulley rope to snap so that the weight at the end falls and bonks someone on the head.

Roof-mounted masts

Masts are self-supporting or guyed structures that are used to support the shortwave antenna system. They can be mounted on the ground or on the tops or sides of houses and other buildings. Commercial radio and television masts are also available from a variety of sources. These commercial masts are covered later in this section.

Still, this book isn't about finding the best deal in antennas, it's about building them yourself. A usable short mast can be constructed from a single piece of lumber, such as a 2×3 or a 2×4. These board masts can be conveniently installed on the top of a building and guyed to three corners of the roof. The guy wires should be equally spaced around the mast and broken in two places, once near the mast and once near the connecting point with small ceramic insulators. Figure 5-2 shows a mast of this type and its possible uses in different applications. This type of mast is not extremely sturdy, so it should be kept relatively short, and it should only be used to support small vertical or wire antennas. The guy wires should be connected about ⅔ or ¾ of the way up the mast. Use screw eyes on the mast to provide simple, strong connection points for the guy wires. Screw eyes should also be mounted at the corners of the roof (but not through the roof) for the bottom ends of the guy wires.

In addition to having guy wires, the antenna mast should also be secured at its bottom, where it meets the roof. You might try a heavy dose of an industrial- or construction-grade adhesive where the mast meets the roof, to prevent the bottom of the mast from "kicking out." Be very careful walking on and hammering anything into a roof—they are much easier to damage than they are to fix. Trying to find the leak in our bathroom ceiling (under several of my antennas) has been maddening, to say the least! Because of potential roof damage, and also because I don't really trust guy wires alone, I would rather use something to help brace the mast. One possible method would be to brace the mast against a chimney, but make sure that it isn't a fireplace or woodstove chimney or you could burn the house down! Another possibility would be to brace the antenna mast against the side of the house. Of course, the mast and the bracing must be secure or it could fall and cause extensive damage.

As mentioned previously, wooden roof-mounted antenna masts have the disadvantages of being a bit heavy, which can cause roof or house damage if they fall. In addition, the wood is prone to warping quickly or rotting after a few years. Treated lumber is an answer to the rotting problem, but it is heavier and it often splits and twists after a few years.

When installing mast sections on a V-sloped roof, do not depend on your balance alone to maintain proper footing. A well-anchored ladder lying on the roof and secured at the roof's peak makes an excellent work platform. Like anything this dangerous, I can't emphasize enough that you must be very careful and make sure that your ropes are properly secured. My father has been a full-time housepainter for 37 years. One time a few years ago, he was painting the roof of a barn using this method when the securing ropes cut loose. He fell about 35 to 40 feet and was very fortunate to survive the accident.

A fall from even a low roof can be very serious or even fatal, so make absolutely certain of your work area and footing platform. Another area that people often ignore is that of roof support stresses. Check over prints and drawings of the building on which a mast is to be mounted. Make sure that the mast and any antennas connected to it will not present too great of a weight on the roof, which could cause an accident or damage. If you have any doubt about your roof's capacity, check with a local contractor or building inspector. Make certain the roof can support the mast weight as well as the weight of any workers who will be helping with the installation.

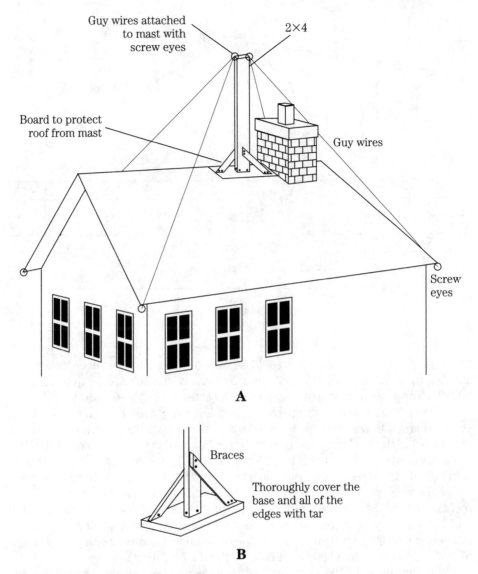

Guy wires attached
to mast with
screw eyes

2×4

Board to protect
roof from mast

Guy wires

Screw
eyes

A

Braces

Thoroughly cover the
base and all of the
edges with tar

B

5-2 The mounting position of a very simple wooden mast on a house roof (A) and close
up (B).

The PVC mast

My favorite idea for a lightweight roof-mounted mast is to use one made out of
PVC (polyvinylchloride) pipe (Fig. 5-3). As you might know, PVC is a type of plastic,
and pipes made of PVC are very lightweight and inexpensive. For these reasons, PVC
pipe is very popular with plumbers. It can be found in any hardware or construction
supply store.

PVC is available in many different lengths and diameters. Although other sizes
would also be workable, the best bet would be to use 2" to 3" diameter PVC at 10' to

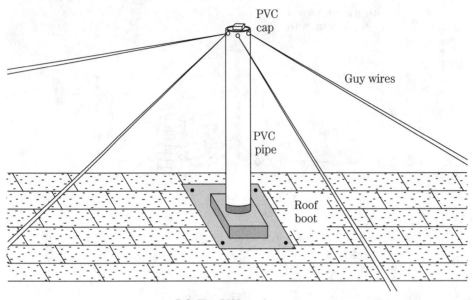

PVC
cap

Guy wires

PVC
pipe

Roof
boot

5-3 The PVC roof mast.

20' long. Of course, PVC couplers could be used to make the mast even taller. Considering the flexibility of PVC, and that a 20' mast would already be approximately 40' off of the ground on an average house, it's best to be satisfied with the 20' mast.

Another inexpensive hardware store special is the *roof boot*. Roof boots are used to seal leaks around sewage ventilation pipes that vent out of the roof. Using a roof boot at the bottom of the PVC mast can prevent water from leaking into the roof (if the PVC would happen to cut the shingles), and it can prevent the bottom of the PVC mast from "kicking out" or sliding on the roof (which also keeps the roofing from being damaged). Make sure when you purchase a roof boot that you pick one that fits the angle of your roof and also the diameter of your PVC pipe. Using a roof boot that doesn't fit either the roof or the pipe is an almost sure way to cause a leak. To further prevent the roofing from being damaged, you can cut a small piece of innertube rubber or a piece of a tire to fit at the inside bottom of the roof boot (under the PVC mast).

When installing the PVC mast, it's best to fit the roof boot over one end of the pipe and scoot it down to the bottom. Twenty feet is a long way to scoot a boot, so you might want to push the boot up onto the pipe a few feet, then pull the boot back down into place, making sure that the rubber seal is smooth and back in place around the pipe.

Next, drill holes in the pipe for the guy wires. You can use either three or four guy wires (spaced evenly) per section. Obviously, four guy wires would give the mast more support than three, so choose what you think will do the best job under your circumstances. The holes in the pipe should be staggered a few inches apart vertically so that the length of PVC remains strong. For a 20' mast, I recommend guying near the top and the middle of the pipe. If the mast is less than 15', it probably only needs to be guyed at one place. If you plan to use the mast for holding a wire antenna, also drill a hole for that near the top.

Because the mast is so light and will be supporting only light loads, you should be able to use nylon rope (rather than steel rope) for the guy wires. Nylon rope that is anywhere from ¼" to ½" thick should work fine. When you drill the holes in the mast, pick a bit size that is just slightly larger in diameter than the size of the rope that you are using. If you want to save a few feet of rope, you can use the Pythagoraean theorem to determine exactly how much you need for each guy wire (Fig. 5-4):

$$Z^2 = X^2 + Y^2$$

where
X and Y are each 90° sides of the triangle
Z is the hypotenuse (the guy wire)

In order for the Pythagoraean theorem to work for measuring your guy wires, you must choose the point on your roof where the boot and mast assembly will be mounted, and you must measure the roof from the mast mark to the points where each guy wire will be attached at the roof edge (distance Y). Because few people have perfectly square roofs, you need to measure distance Y each time.

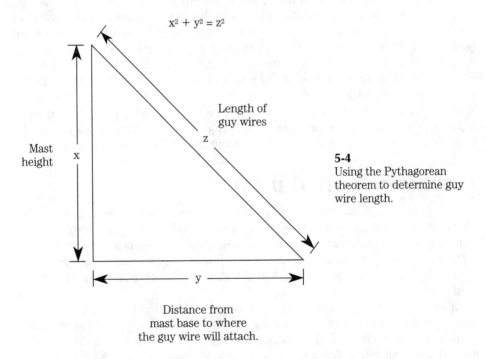

$x^2 + y^2 = z^2$

Length of
guy wires

z

Mast
height

x

5-4
Using the Pythagorean
theorem to determine guy
wire length.

y

Distance from
mast base to where
the guy wire will attach.

After you have taken so much time to make sure that your measurements are perfect, add about 3' extra onto each guy wire for knotting and securing purposes. Next, cut the ropes to the proper lengths. For each rope, slide about 1' into the hole that it is to be secured in. Then, slide a flat washer onto the end of the rope, to the inside of the pipe (Fig. 5-5). Knot the rope several times and be sure that it is fastened securely. Do the same for the rest of the guy wires. For the wire antenna, fasten about 15' to 20' of rope in the same manner that the other guy wires were installed.

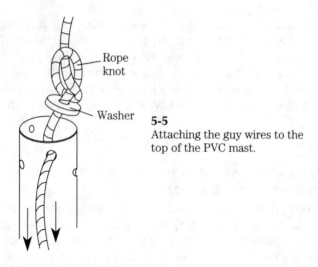

Rope knot

Washer

5-5
Attaching the guy wires to the top of the PVC mast.

At each point at the edge of the roof where a guy wire is to be attached, secure a screw eye that is large enough to handle both the size of the rope and the strain of the weight that is being guyed. If you are using the mast to raise a small vertical antenna, install it on the top now. Whether or not you use a vertical antenna on the top, make sure that the top of the PVC pipe is capped, or you will soon wind up with a 20' cylinder full of water on your roof. With some help from a friend or two, take the mast assembly (with the roof boot and guy ropes attached) to the roof and mount it. The mast should be held in place by one person while the other two tie the guy wires tight. Once everything is in place and the mast seems to be straight, nail down the boot to the roof. Then, either tar or roof-cement the edges to keep it waterproofed.

Ground-mounted masts

Roof-mounted masts have a real advantage in the sense that your roof is probably anywhere from 15' to 35' above the ground to start with. If you want your antenna to 50' above the ground, a mast on a house probably needs to be only about 25' high. On the other hand, heavy-do-it-yourself projects on the roof of your house are dangerous—much more dangerous than installing the same type of structure in your yard.

Personally, I am not particularly fond of large ground-mounted antenna masts because the guy wires stretch across about 40' or 50' of the yard and really hamper outdoor activities. I much prefer mounting antennas in trees and on the house—they are much less obtrusive this way. Ground-mounted masts seem to be most useful if the location is somewhere in the plains states, where large acreage is generally common and trees are scarce.

The major components in a successful homemade ground-mounted antenna mast are guy wires, guy supports, and the antenna mast itself. You might also consider the antenna to be part of the system as well, but it's not so much a part of the mast as it is the whole reason to build the mast. The guy wires are a key factor in the success of any homemade ground-mounted antenna mast.

Guy wires

For most lightweight masts up to 45', stranded steel wire is preferred for guy wires. Nylon rope was used to guy the PVC mast, but that was because the mast was short and lightweight. Steel wire is carried by most hardware stores and is usually recommended for antenna mast erection purposes. Several lengths of this cable can be overlapped and run in parallel for added strength when used for masts that need to withstand high-wind conditions or are higher than 45'.

Under certain operating conditions, guy wires can act as an antenna. This situation is not usually advantageous, because it often detracts from the performance of the main antenna system. Strain insulators are usually adequate for most frequencies. The only type of insulator that should be considered for guying purposes is the *ceramic egg* variety. This type of strain insulator does not allow the guy wire to separate—even if the ceramic insulating material shatters. The two sections of guy wiring are insulated from each other but are intertwined within the egg insulator (Fig. 5-6).

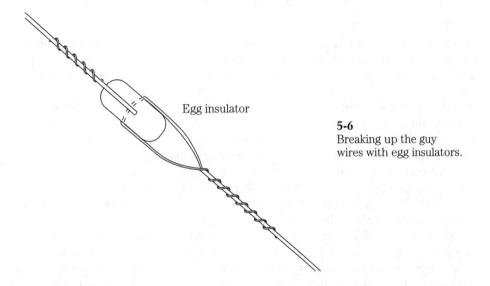

Egg insulator

5-6
Breaking up the guy
wires with egg insulators.

Anchoring guy wires is best accomplished by connecting them to pipes driven into the ground (Fig. 5-7A) or to "dead man" supports that have been buried in the ground. For best results using pipes, bend the last few inches of the pipe over (at approximately a 45° angle). Then, pound them into the ground (with the bent side facing away from the antenna) with a sledgehammer. Having the end of the pipe bent helps keep the guy wire from slipping off the end of the support. Also, if you pound the ends of the pipes to the ground, it prevents those who walk through the yard from getting nasty scrapes and bruises on their ankles. As many times as I have tripped on tent stakes, this is a real advantage.

It is possible to guy masts to a convenient tree or building, but you must carefully choose and install both mast and guy wire. If you improperly choose or install your guy wires to one or more of these objects, you could damage or uproot a tree or

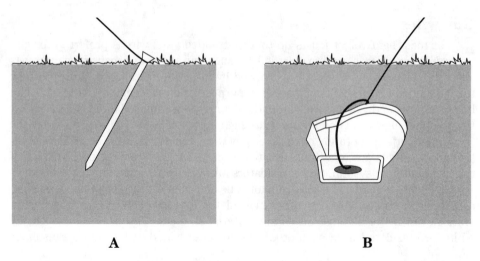

A   **B**

5-7 Guy wire supports: A) a ground stake and B) a buried "dead man" (a toilet, in this case).

create some havoc at your house. For small masts that support very light antenna systems, a 4' length of pipe driven into the ground at a pronounced angle usually provides adequate anchoring. Choose your materials carefully when building these anchors.

The "dead man" support is merely a large piece of metal or concrete that has been buried about 3 or 4 feet deep. Some objects that make great dead man supports are large car parts (such as wheels, bumpers, engine blocks, etc.), old toilets (Fig. 5-7B), and concrete sidewalk slabs. One of the great aspects about using large junk to support your antenna masts is that you can get rid of this stuff for free and it can serve a practical purpose (as opposed to sitting for decades or centuries in a landfill).

Faulty pipes used to anchor guy wires have been known to fly out of the ground at lethal velocities when a large gust of wind provided sudden pressure. All too often, an anxious builder simply drives a few tent stakes into the ground to anchor the mast and antenna system that he or she has spent days building, only to find the entire system lying on the ground the next day. All materials, no matter how small, play an important role in the construction of your antenna and antenna support systems.

Telephone poles

One of the most functional types of masts is the simple *telephone pole* (Fig. 5-8). This is the type of mast that is used by the power and utility companies to support the weight of telephone and power cables. You should only use unused telephone poles, not those that are still in service by the public utility companies. Using these in-service poles is not only very dangerous and illegal, but the results will be poor because the receiving antenna will pick up so much power line noise.

Most telephone poles are sturdy enough to support even the largest of SWL antenna systems and in almost every case no guy wires are required. Telephone poles have the additional advantage of being climbable and many have steel pegs that are used as steps to get to the top without difficulty. Telephone poles, though never very

5-8
A television antenna mounted
on a telephone pole mast.

commonly used by shortwave listeners and amateurs, were occasionally used years ago, before the days of aluminum masts and towers. These days, few people use telephone poles because they are heavy, more difficult to install than just about any type of mast, and because few people want one (or more) massive, dark brown poles towering over their yard.

At one time, telephone poles could be readily obtained from the local utility companies for next to nothing. These were the poles that had seen much service and were no longer usable for their original purpose, but for SWL antenna requirements they still had many useful years left in them. New telephone poles are a different story; depending on the height and the part of the country where purchased, a standard weatherproofed telephone pole can run several dollars per foot. Poles of 30' to 50' are the best length to use in an SWL capacity, but remember that about 1/10 of the length must be set in the ground for proper stability. Sandy or loose soil conditions require that an additional length be buried.

A telephone pole is a heavy item, much too large for a single person to install. However, several able-bodied shortwave listeners can install one in a reasonable length of time through the use of hoisting ropes and a truck or Jeep. Local lumber companies can also install your telephone pole mast, but the bill for this type of installation often runs into a large percentage of the original cost of the pole.

When a telephone pole or any mast that does not use guy wires anchored to the ground is installed, a means of grounding should be considered. Large-gauge aluminum or copper wire can be run from the top of the mast to the ground and then be tied to a ground pipe that is driven at least 6' into the soil. This ground wire can be installed on a telephone pole before installation so that the bottom portion of the pole and ground wire are buried at the same time. The ground wire (heavy gauge, #8 or larger) should be stapled to the mast every foot or so. If you properly ground the telephone pole mast, lightning strikes can be avoided in most instances. If lightning should strike, most of the electricity will be diverted to the ground and away from your antenna system, receiver, and house.

Aluminum masts

The wooden masts described earlier must be considered short-term arrangements. Rain, snow, wind, and other elements eventually wear down any wooden structure no matter how well it is protected from water with weatherproofing materials. Telephone poles are an exception, but they are cumbersome and sometimes expensive. A permanent and more lightweight mast material is *standard aluminum tubing* (Fig. 5-9).

5-9 An aluminum mast.

Television antennas have long been supported by aluminum, and many antennas installed 30 years ago are still supported on their original masts. Your local television shop or hardware store can probably supply you with an aluminum mast. Some radio and television antenna masts are commercially available for prices that range from reasonable to expensive. If you want to find the least expensive mast available (including those that you can build yourself), you might consider checking the weekly "shopper" papers for used television masts. Now that cable television has conquered off-air television in the cities and large towns, old television antennas and masts can be picked up for almost nothing. Before you agree to take a mast, you should probably make sure that it has already been taken off the roof or has been disassembled. Otherwise, you could damage (or be blamed for damage to) the roof or the house.

A good rule of thumb is to use the standard television antennas mast materials only for lightweight antenna systems. The medium- and heavy-duty antenna mast materials can be used for larger antennas. Proper guying techniques must be used for aluminum masts. If a section is improperly guyed, it will bend and you will be forced to replace it. Never use a bent section—even if it has been straightened. Bent sections are much weaker than the rest of the mast. The bent section will eventually bend or break. Then, it will have to be replaced at the cost of time and money because the whole antenna and support system have to come down. Galvanized heavy-duty tubing in slip-together pieces is available at most hardware stores, and it makes excellent permanent and portable mast material. It is strong enough to support the largest antenna systems, and it is not very expensive.

If you purchase a commercial aluminum mast or tower, be sure to follow the directions for installing it. If you find a good deal on a used aluminum mast or tower, check with a local television shop to see if it has directions for assembly/disassembly of that particular type of antenna mast or tower. If you can find the instructions, you'll probably save a considerable amount of time and energy.

Few people want to build their own aluminum antenna masts, because buying a used mast is less expensive than building your own. Aluminum welding is beyond the scope of this book, so if you are a welder and decide to take that route, be sure to follow safe antenna construction and installation practices.

A simple ground-mounted mast

Thus far, except for the telephone pole mast, this chapter has covered only rooftop antenna masts. The PVC mast can be installed on the ground, but because PVC is flexible, it's best to keep the mast short. Thus, the ground-mounted peak height would probably be too low to be very useful.

As I stated earlier, wooden masts are heavy and prone to rotting, cracking, splitting, and warping. As a result, few people use wooden masts anymore. Most of the magazines and books that featured wooden masts did so before 1960. Although these masts are antiquated by today's technology, they can still be useful because the cost of new towers is so high. One annoying problem with wooden towers is liability. If your tower is taken out in a hurricane, tornado, or tropical storm, you could very well be sued if the mast smashes through your neighbor's fence, tree, or yard. These days, I wouldn't be too surprised if someone sabotaged a tower so that it would fall on the property and they could sue the owner. Stranger lawsuits have occurred!

Because of the lawsuit problem, wooden masts are best utilized if you own a few acres (or more) of land and can install them in places where they can't fall on anyone else's property. Otherwise you could be taking a big risk. As the old adage goes, "you can't be too careful." If you missed the safety notice at the beginning of the chapter, go back and read it.

Figure 5-10 shows a strong and simple wooden mast that depends on a buried section to provide stability. This mast can be extended to about 40', but it does not require the lateral space or extra lumber that some of the older tower-style wooden masts required.

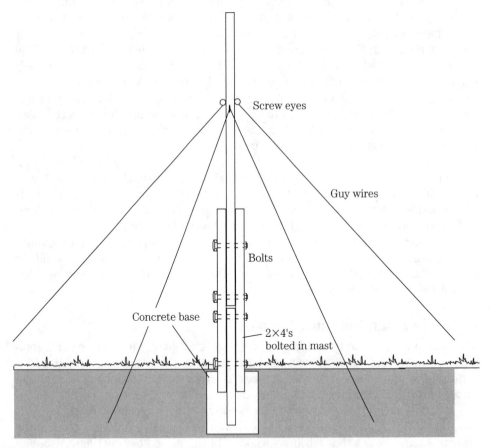

5-10 The wooden ground-mounted mast.

The simple wooden mast covered in this section only requires four 20' long 2 × 4s, eight carriage bolts, 6 (or more) large eye bolts, approximately 300' of steel guy wire, and approximately 50 to 100 pounds of quick-setting concrete mix. All of the 2-×-4 boards should be straight and free of knots, splits, and defects. For extra protection against rotting, but also much greater weight, use treated lumber.

Because of the length of the antenna mast (40' total), you should take the materials outside to start working on them. If you have free space more than 20' long in your basement, you might want to paint the boards indoors. Use a good-quality exterior paint and cover the ends several times because the ends really soak up the paint. Depending on the weather, this might be a good time to go out to the point where you want the mast installed and dig a hole that's about 4' or 5' deep and several feet wide. When the 2×4s have dried, the weather is sunny, the hole is dug, and you have a friend or two along to help you, take the mast materials outside.

Now it's time to start assembling the mast. Start by marking the bolt holes for where the topmost section of the mast meets the pair of 2×4s that will sandwich it on either side. Drill the holes and make sure that they all align properly. Then, put the top three boards together and run the first bolt through. Next, pull out the 2×4, which becomes the bottom anchoring portion for the mast, and do the same. Make sure that there is approximately a ½" gap in the center between the topmost part of the mast and the bottommost part. This space allows for contracting and expanding in the summer and winter. Now that the four pieces of the mast are attached to each other, it should be a relatively easy process to lift the mast off the ground and drill the other six bolt holes through the three boards. This process ensures that the bolt holes all align. Then, bolt the boards together in the rest of these places.

Install the eye bolts with the equal spacing around the top of the mast and around the center of the mast (where the topmost mast section meets the two lower boards). When planning the length of the guy wires, make sure that they extend out from the base of the mast by at least 60% of the height of the mast. See the roof-mounted PVC mast (earlier in this chapter) for basic instructions. Run the guy wires through the eye bolts and attach them fast to the top of the mast with cable clamps. Don't forget to install any vertical antennas or connections for wire antennas now!

Put a fairly large, flat rock in the bottom of the hole and then, with some help from your friends, move the mast and place the bottom of it on the rock and slowly raise it into a vertical position. One person should stay with the mast and hold it vertical while the others connect the guy wires to the guy supports and tighten them with the turnbuckles. The turnbuckles should be tightened slowly and evenly around the mast. If one guy wire is tightened first, the mast could very well end up crooked. Periodically check the mast with a level to make sure that it is straight.

Once the mast is straight and all of the guy wires have some tension, it's time to mix up the concrete. Just-add-water concrete mix is my choice in this situation. Mix it together and pour it in the hole around the mast. Then, walk around to the guy wires in a clockwise direction and give each turnbuckle a turn or two (just like tightening the bolts on the wheel of a car). Once the guy wires seem to be tightened adequately, the mast is finished. Just don't overtighten the guy wires or too much strain will be placed on the guy supports and the top of the mast.

A properly constructed and treated wooden mast or tower can be expected to give at least several years of dependable service. I know of some wooden masts that have remained structurally sound for more than a decade. Still, you should regularly inspect the mast for splitting, warping, or rotting. When the first signs of deterioration are discovered, there usually is more extensive damage hidden from view. Then, you'll need to completely replace the structure in a short period of time.

Other masts and structures

Like antennas, homemade antenna towers and masts are often engineering marvels that are designed to coincide and compensate for a peculiarity of the environment. For example, some people have no yard, so a roof-mounted mast is appropriate. Others have plenty of space, so many ground-mounted masts can be installed. Often, especially during the Depression, a lack of general funds prompted hobbyists to create brilliant and alternative methods for building antenna masts and towers. For some of these towers, it was amazing that they remained in the air. But others were solid *and* made brilliant use of materials. Only a few of these are mentioned here—not necessarily for you to build, but to be an inspiration to your creative thinking. Figure 5-11 shows an old mast with a new use.

Probably my favorite tower was covered in a 1937 issue of *QST*, in an article and written by James Millen, the genius who helped propel the National Radio Company and who later formed his own company. Millen and some of his radio friends designed a tower that was built entirely out of 75¢ wooden ladders (Fig. 5-12). Three ladders were bolted together edgewise into a section and these sections were also bolted together. The mast was set in concrete in the ground and extended to a height of 50'. At the time, the mast was amazing because it was inexpensive, relatively easy to build, and climbable. This mast must have had a large impact on the design of future aluminum and steel towers (Fig. 5-13).

5-11
A television antenna mounted on an old amateur radio tower. The tower itself is probably at least 40 years old.

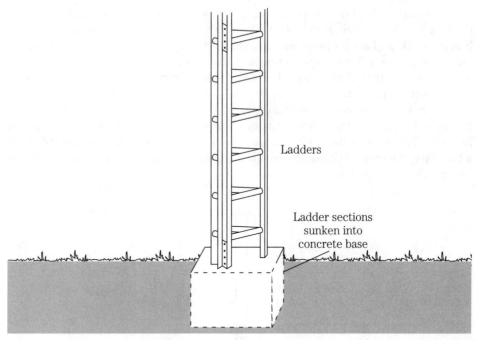

Ladders

Ladder sections
sunken into
concrete base

5-12 The base of the wooden ladder mast.

5-13
A commercial steel tower.

One mast that's much more feasible by today's standards is the pipe mast. Old military surplus mobile masts of this type are available from some radio supply houses, such as Fair Radio Sales. You can either buy an old military version or build one yourself. These pipe antennas usually consist of a few segments of aluminum or steel pipe that fit together and are held in place at each joint with one or two cotter pins (Fig. 5-14). The base of the antenna is a pipe segment with a hinged spike on the end. The spiked end is pounded into the ground, the segments and cotter pins are added, the guy wires are attached, and the assembly is lifted up. The one standard military mast is 40' high and is built to withstand quite a bit of nasty weather. Carefully designed pipe masts have been constructed well beyond the 40' height.

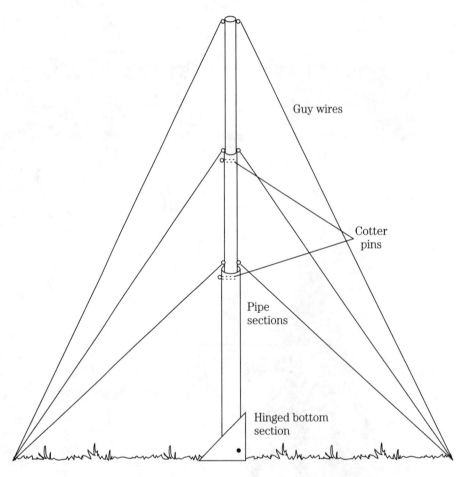

Guy wires

Cotter pins

Pipe sections

Hinged bottom section

5-14 The sectional pipe mast.

One amateur operator designed a tree mast in the 1960s (Fig. 5-15). Because he lived in dense woods, he had no room to install a tower and the area around his

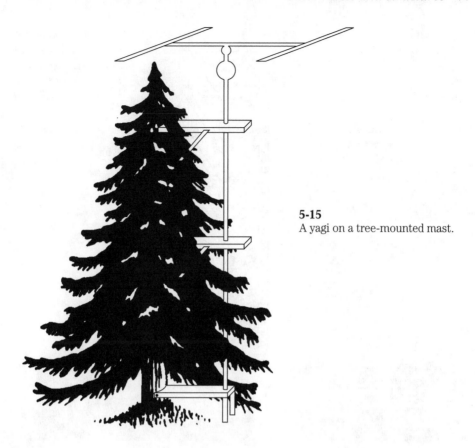

5-15
A yagi on a tree-mounted mast.

house wasn't clear for wire antennas. So, he topped a pine tree in his yard and installed a few platforms down the side of the tree. With a plumb bob, he found a straight line down from the top and drilled holes in the platforms at those points. Then, he ran a long pipe through the holes and connected a rotor to the bottom and a quad antenna to the top. Considering the height of the pine tree, I have no idea how he got the quad or the length of pipe to the top of the tree. Personally, I would rather install a nice longwire antenna than dangle from the top of a 100' pine tree while attempting to attach a quad to the end of a pipe!

The last antenna tower in this chapter is the most curious, ingenious, and possibly dangerous of the lot—it was made out of metal shelving edges (Fig. 5-16). These metal shelving edges are lengths of galvanized steel with bolt holes. With some cutting, the finished product was assembled and bolted together. It looked like a life-sized Erector set model of a TV tower! The dangers in building this tower are that none of the parts were welded together and also that the edges were only intended for shelving. Still, it was an interesting and creative effort!

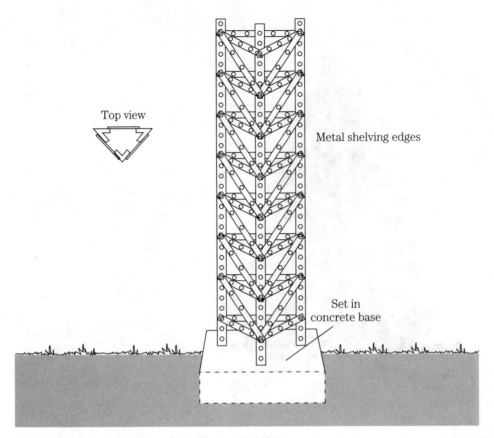

Top view

Metal shelving edges

Set in
concrete base

5-16 The metal shelving mast.

6
CHAPTER

Grounding and lightning protection

Proper grounding and lightning protection procedures are often neglected by short-wave listeners and sometimes even by radio amateurs. These procedures are particularly important for radio amateurs, who generally have antennas that are much higher than those of shortwave listeners. The increased height makes them more vulnerable to a lightning strike. Also, grounded antennas are much more efficient than those that are ungrounded. The difference might not be huge when receiving, but it is noticeable when transmitting. If a transmitter is operating without a ground, much of the power is wasted—turned from RF (radio frequency) power into heat, which is absorbed by the soil near the antenna.

If you are using an outdoor antenna or (especially) a tower or mast, you might be required to have a ground system that has been constructed according to local safety ordinances. Not following these ordinances can put you at odds with the law. You can be fined continuously until you install a ground system that conforms to local guidelines. These ordinances weren't merely passed to restrict your personal freedoms; they were passed to protect you and prevent the construction of antennas or other lightning-attracting devices without adequate grounding systems.

If you had an ungrounded antenna that got struck by lightning and started a fire in your house, chances are that your insurance wouldn't cover the bill. In the view of the insurance company, you installed a device that attracted massive destruction. Would they be wrong?

Ground systems

Antennas and supporting structures should be provided with a means of grounding even when they are not in use. High charges of static electricity can build up on a large antenna system, which could cause damage to a shortwave receiver during an electrical storm. Even wooden masts and towers can conduct electricity—especially when they are drenched by heavy rains. Lightning strikes are rare, but they can be avoided in most cases by taking proper precautions.

A lightning strike is caused by a sufficient buildup of electrical charge in the atmosphere, which eventually arcs to ground. This occurrence is much like a voltage point in an electronic circuit arcing to the chassis of your radio when insulation breaks down on a wire. When a large structure is grounded, electricity in the atmosphere travels down the structure to ground before a current of sufficient magnitude can build up to cause an actual lightning strike. Therefore, a grounded antenna can protect surrounding structures from strikes, instead of being a high-risk source for strikes.

Wooden masts, towers, and telephone poles can be protected by installing a length of copper or copper-clad wire from top to bottom down one side of the structure with a connection at the base to a ground rod (Fig. 6-1). This grounding wire should be of #8 or larger. The larger wire sizes provide increased protection. A completely straight path from the top of a mast to the ground stake is essential to cut down on the amount of resistance incurred in the length of the grounding wire. If a larger size is not available, install two or three small-diameter conductors and provide a straight and clear path in all cases.

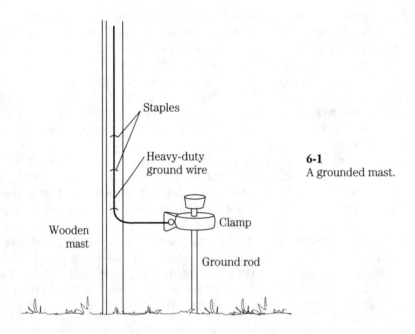

Staples

Heavy-duty
ground wire

Wooden
mast

Clamp

Ground rod

6-1
A grounded mast.

The ground rod should also be either solid copper or copper-clad. To be safe, you should use a 4' to 6' long (or longer) ground rod or pipe. Use a sledgehammer to drive the ground rod or pipe into the soil. Depending on where you live, this might be a problem, particularly if you are trying to drive a flimsy copper pipe into rocky soil. I know how this can be a problem, because I grew up in the mountains of southern Pennsylvania, where rocks seem to be more plentiful than soil.

One solution that noted antenna expert Joe Carr covered in an article for *Modern Electronics*, was to use a hydraulic drill (Fig. 6-2). It sounds complicated and expensive, but the whole system was really rather simple. The antenna makers fitted a plumbing T onto the top end of the pipe. They capped one side of the T and connected the other side to a garden hose. They turned on the garden hose and then pushed down on the pipe. The water pressure blasted the pipe into the ground. I have seen this method of hydraulic drilling used in old hippie back-to-the-land and homesteading books from the 1970s, but I never saw it applied to installing ground pipes before this article. Using this sort of creativity and ingenuity could make an otherwise marginal antenna system quite successful.

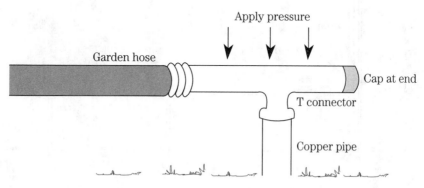

6-2 Using a hydraulic drill to sink a ground pipe.

Dry and rocky soil, which does not provide good ground conductivity, can be improved by installing a buried ground system at the base of the structure to be grounded. It is made exactly like the antenna ground system described earlier. The best protection is provided by using the greatest amount of wire feasible in the ground system.

Alternative methods can be used to improve the ground conductivity. Some people also bury rock salt in the area where the grounding wires make contact with the soil. I don't think that burying salt is a great idea, because salt can kill vegetation. Also, salt corrodes the radials, raising ground resistance and eventually destroying the wires! Having wire strung through the property is bad enough without having a barren yard. I even know of one hobbyist who, before he transmits, hoses down the area where his ground system is buried to increase the ground conductivity! Soaking the area around a ground system might work fairly well, but it isn't very practical if you use your radio regularly.

Ground system wires and connections to ground rods and pipes should never be just soldered. Instead, they should be bonded with a transit clamp, which can be purchased at most hardware and electrical supply stores, then soldered. Check any connections periodically for signs of corrosion and breaks. When one side of a dipole antenna is supported by a house or other structure, don't depend on the ceramic insulator to provide electrical isolation. Even a small lightning strike will jump over this insulator.

For even better protection, one or more extra ground rods can be installed in tandem (Fig. 6-3). These extra rods should all be interconnected, using clamps that are connected together with ground strapping. For best results, additional ground rods should be spaced as far apart as they are long. This system has more area in contact with the ground, which makes it more effective.

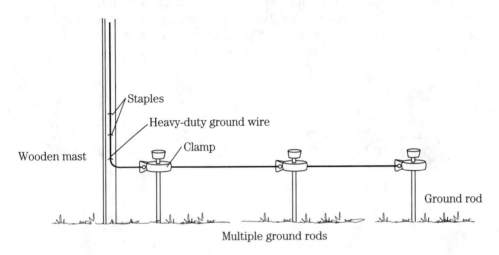

Multiple ground rods

6-3 Multiple ground rods at a mast.

Like antennas, ground systems can also be tuned to a proper operating frequency. Because tuned grounds aren't necessary for good receiving performance, this section only covers a little of the actual practice of installing a tuned ground. Tuned grounds are handy for amateur radio operators or CB enthusiasts who specialize in using one frequency band. As described in chapter 2, a number of quarter-wavelength wire ground radials can be run out from a ground rod (Fig. 6-4). The optimum number of ground radials is 120, but who would bother to dump thousands of feet of wire into the ground on a matter that makes very little difference in reception? The general concensus for the best minimum number of radials is 16. These radials should be buried a few inches under the ground for maximum efficiency.

Although it's not a homemade project, MFJ Enterprises designed an artificial ground that can be used by radio enthusiasts who are restricted to living in apartments or condos and are unable to install a proper ground (Fig. 6-5). The MFJ-931 is a small box with a meter and a few knobs that you can use to tune the "ground" for maximum transmitting efficiency. The MFJ-931 is handy for ham radio operators who want to use a ground-dependent antenna (such as a vertical or a longwire). However, this artificial ground is *not* intended to replace the ground rods or pipes at the bottom of a tower! Attempting to use it in this manner could result in a variety of hazards, the least being that the artificial ground would blow up.

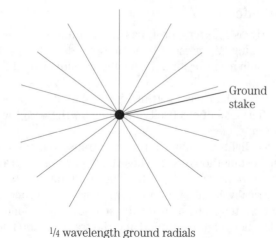

6-4
A system of ground radials.

¼ wavelength ground radials

6-5
The MFJ 931 artificial ground.

Lightning protection

Lightning is the greatest natural hazard to radio hobbyists. Many antennas, especially the tall verticals, beams, and quads, are extremely vulnerable to lightning strikes. Of course, lightning is extremely dangerous—both directly (explosive electric force) and indirectly (fire). As a result, you must take every precaution to make sure that your antennas are safe.

The first good safety measure is to prevent lightning from hitting your tower or mast (assuming that you have either). When the danger of lightning strikes is eminent, large masses of air become positively or negatively charged. As a positive charge builds up in a cloud, for example, a negative charge is also increasing on the tower or mast. When the charge reaches the saturation point, it will discharge (lightning) and fry your tower or mast.

In order to prevent lightning from striking your mast or tower, you must keep it from building up a huge charge during an electrical storm. The best method of doing this is to install a lightning rod on the top of the tower or mast so that it is higher than the top and the antennas. The end of the lightning rod is sharply pointed, so it prevents a large charge from building up. This in turn prevents lightning from striking the tower, and it should even provide some additional protection for the area near the tower.

Keeping the lightning outside

Other antennas are not nearly as lightning-prone as the tall antennas—especially for standard shortwave listening. My present home antenna is a droopy 125' longwire. With all of the tall television masts around the neighborhood, I would think that this antenna could probably stay where it is for several hundred years and still not get hit by lightning. Although the chances of getting hit are slim, it is a possibility. And the thoughts of a large, fiery ball of electricity hurdling up the wire toward me aren't especially pleasant either.

Use a device to ground out the lightning on an antenna or transmission line before it can reach your house. The best method to keep these huge power surges away from your house is to use a *lightning arrestor* (Fig.6-6). The lightning arrestor is a tube that physically, but not electrically, breaks the run of transmission line and provides a connection to the ground system. The arrestor doesn't actually ground the antenna because a small gap is left between the ground and the transmission line. If a lightning strike occurs and a blast of electricity is traveling up the transmission line, it probably won't reach the shack of someone with a properly installed lightning arrestor. Instead, it will take the shortest route to ground by arcing over the lightning arrestor terminals and discharging into the ground system. Some of the more expensive models provide excellent protection for all but the most severe lightning strikes.

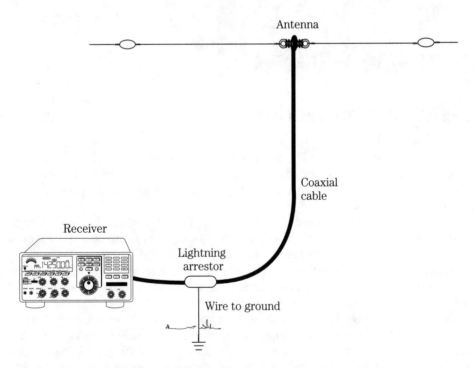

6-6 Using a lightning arrestor in an antenna system.

Several commercially built lightning protection devices are on the market. Some of these devices are PL-259 connectors with a screwed insert on the sleeve so that it can be grounded. I don't recommend these PL-259 connectors because the lightning charge would already be in the house before it would run to ground—sort of like allowing a tiger into your house to buy you time to think of a proper way to dispose of it. However, if a way can be found to temporarily remove the transmission line from the building housing the receiving equipment, equal protection should result without the added expense of purchasing a commercial unit.

Even if electrical storms are not common in a certain area, adequate lightning protection for all antennas and structural supports is a must for safe shortwave listening operations. You can obtain additional information by consulting the electrical codes and guidelines set up by the city or county where you are planning to install your antennas.

7
CHAPTER

Antenna
construction projects

Thus far, this book has covered everything about shortwave-listening antennas, except actually building them. The first chapter did cover a few simple makeshift and beginner's antennas, but this chapter is the first that pulls out construction projects for outdoor antennas, and antennas that can be used for receiving *and* transmitting (if you're a radio amateur or a CBer). This chapter deals exclusively with the construction of antennas taken from the basic designs and theory studied in earlier chapters. Most of these are a bit more (in some cases, much more) complicated than those in chapter 1. Still, each antenna generally can be broken down into one or two basic designs or a combination of several different types of antenna systems.

As I have already emphasized at various points throughout this book, there is no single best antenna for everyone. Every listener has different needs, and the most appropriate antenna is one that will fulfill the listening needs and will be within the bounds of a listener's capabilities. For example, I would love to have log-periodic antenna (a type of directional antenna) cut for 1000 kHz on a rotatable tower. However, this antenna would cover an acre or so with many elements and it would probably require hundreds of thousands of dollars. I can't build this antenna because I don't have enough land, money, or construction skill. Also, it would be unsightly and illegal in the town where I live. These factors all come into play when you choose an antenna system.

The appendix contains an element length chart that can be used to determine the correct dimensions of the element or elements of the antenna system. This chart lists the proper lengths for antenna elements at shortwave and amateur frequencies that span the shortwave band. You can choose the frequency or frequencies that you use most often and design the system from the information and figure supplies for that portion of the shortwave band. If you want to cut an antenna for a particular frequency band, it is best to cut the antenna elements for the approximate middle of the band. That way, the entire frequency band can be covered. Multiband antennas, which receive on several different frequencies with equal efficiency, usually require several different elements—each cut to a different length (using the same chart). When frequency coverage on bands not listed in the element length chart is desired, a formula can be used to determine the proper dimensions.

Each construction project provides a formula in a form similar to:

$$L = \frac{468}{f(\text{MHz})}$$

This might appear at first glance to be a complicated algebraic equation that only college professors can understand, but when each letter is explained the meaning is quite simple. L is the symbol for element length in feet, f is the desired operating frequency in megahertz, and 468 is the number that is arrived at through mathematical computations. For antenna-trimming purposes, its derivation is not of further concern. The sample formula shown states that the length of the antenna element is equal to 468 divided by the desired operating frequency of the antenna in megahertz. Appendix A provides an example of how a formula is used to compute element length. The frequency of 7 MHz requires an element length of almost 67' for this type of antenna. Any frequency in the entire radio spectrum can be substituted for 7 MHz, and the correct antenna element length for that frequency can be accurately determined.

Whenever possible, the most common and readily available parts have been chosen, but you can make substitutions if other types of materials are already on hand or can be obtained more easily. When making these substitutions, give special consideration to the mechanical strength of the materials used. When substituting heavier components than those recommended, direct special attention to the guying and support materials. Heavy-duty construction usually means more weight and more stress on the guys and antenna supports. They should be strengthened to adequately handle the strain.

Each item in the material lists was designed and chosen for an antenna system that needs to endure only normal year-round weather conditions. Unusual environments might require antenna modifications. Antennas mounted at a site with high wind conditions on a regular basis must be built to accommodate the added pressure and strain. Salt-water climates pose a problem of corrosion to any metal that is exposed to the air. Areas where heavy snowfall occurs frequently also present a problem—supports bend, wires stretch, and aluminum tubing twists when the weight of the frozen precipitation builds up. These and many other abnormal weather conditions must be accounted for when any antenna system is erected. The great majority of shortwave listeners will find that the material lists are more than adequate for any weather condition, summer or winter, that is likely to be encountered.

By now, you should have a basic understanding of the shortwave antenna system. The next step in the learning process is to build an outdoor antenna project or projects. Mistakes most certainly will occur, but the knowledge gained from these errors will be beneficial for many years to come. In fact, I have found that I learn best by making mistakes—it's a good thing I don't work at a nuclear reactor!

After building a few antennas for optimum shortwave reception, you might even find that antenna building is fun! Antenna-building experience adds up. During my early days of shortwave listening, which were filled with many antenna-building frustrations, I never imagined that I would wind up writing a book on the subject. Over the years, I have gained a real appreciation for antennas. You might find the same appreciation.

The standard dipole and its variations

The standard dipole (and its many variations) has got to be shortwave radio's all-time most-popular antenna (Fig. 7-1). This antenna is very simple, performs very well, and can be configured to save space or change the reception/transmission pattern. Although some amateurs and shortwave listeners move to other antennas, most continue to use a dipole for the lower frequencies (below about 13 MHz). The more complicated antennas are quite handy, but below about 13 MHz they become unwieldy. In these cases, a dipole is a wonderful alternative.

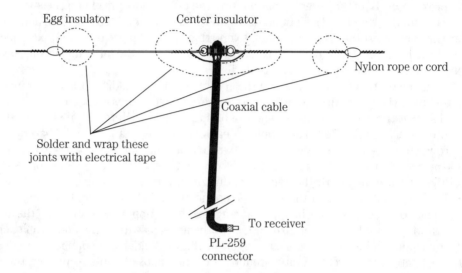

7-1 The dipole antenna.

The dipole is a half-wave wire antenna that is fed in the center with a piece of coaxial cable. Because of the equal-length conductors on either side of the feed point, the dipole was known as a *doublet* in much of the older literature. The term *doublet* is still occasionally used—especially by old-timers and those in foreign countries. Because the dipole is fed by 50-Ω or 75-Ω coaxial cable, there are no problems with matching the antenna to your radio. This is a real problem with many other antennas, and the effects are especially dramatic when transmitting. Some, such as the zepp, allow some of the transmitted signal to get back into the shack and create disturbances (such as electrical shocks at the radio, feedback into telephones, etc.).

The materials needed for a dipole are: plenty of coaxial cable, plenty of wire, plenty of small-diameter rope, rosin-core solder, a center insulator, and two egg insulators. When choosing coaxial cable, RG-58 is fine for listening, but use RG-8X for low- to mid-power transmitting and RG-8 for anything over about 750 watts output. The rope should be small enough to fit through the holes of the end insulators, yet strong enough to support the dipole in the air. Really, any gauge of wire from about #22 up to #6 is fine for dipoles, but the general consensus is that #14 or #16 is the best. Higher-gauge wires are usually used for transmitting. All of the energy from a transmitter is on the very outside of the wire, thus it's best to have the largest diameter possible. This is known as *skin effect*. I have even heard one story from a broadcast engineer who was using over a kilowatt into a small-gauge dipole. The wire gauge was too small to support the high wattage, and the wire heated up. After a few minutes of transmitting, the antenna wire burned up and the remains of the dipole fell to the ground!

Measure and cut the appropriate amount of wire for the band you will use. Always cut the wire a bit longer than specified—you can always cut a longer wire down. Then, cut this wire into two pieces of equal length. Bare about 3" of one end of each wire. Then, cut an appropriate length of coaxial cable. Attach a PL-259 connector to one end of the coax following the instructions in chapter 3. Then, remove approximately 3" of the outer insulation from the other end with a knife (be sure not to cut into the wire braid). Unbraid down one side of the braided shield. When you are finished, twist the braid together into one thick 2"-long piece of wire. Next, move down an inch from the end of the coaxial cable and remove the inner dielectric, leaving 2" of the center conductor exposed.

Tie the prepared antenna-end of the coax around the middle of the center insulator, and twist some wire around the area where the coax crosses itself. Pull up the end so that the center conductor and the braided shield each reach one loop of the center insulator (Fig. 7-2). Then, pull out each piece of wire and loop the bared end through the hole in the center insulator, twisting each around itself on the back side of the center insulator. Then, twist the coax braid in with the wire loop on one side of the insulator, and twist the center conductor in with the wire loop on the other side of the insulator. Solder these twisted connections and make sure that the joints are solid. Using the same technique that you used for wrapping and soldering the antenna wire around the center insulator, strip the antenna wire at the ends, run each through an egg insulator, twist each upon itself, and solder the connections (Fig. 7-3). Tightly wrap electrical tape around all of the exposed joints to protect them from weathering and cracking.

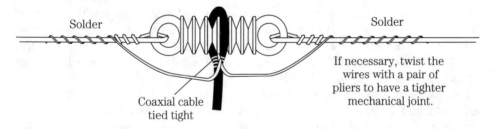

Solder   Solder

If necessary, twist the wires with a pair of pliers to have a tighter mechanical joint.

Coaxial cable tied tight

7-2 A close-up of the center connections of the dipole antenna.

The dipole is ready to go. The reception pattern of the dipole is essentially a doughnut around the wire. In other words, it receives and transmits best from angles that are perpendicular to it. The height above the ground makes a rather dramatic improvement in the performance of the dipole, so you should try to get the antenna as high as possible. Most shortwave listeners have their dipoles fixed about 20' to 40' off the ground. Radio amateurs often get their dipole up to about 60' off the ground

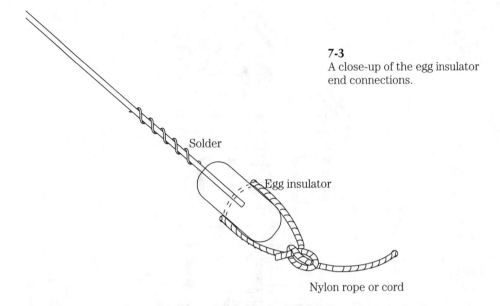

7-3
A close-up of the egg insulator
end connections.

Solder

Egg insulator

Nylon rope or cord

because the height really makes a difference in transmitting effectiveness. When a transmitting antenna is too low to the ground, much of the signal is absorbed by the ground under the antenna. For receiving only, the difference between 30' and 60' is so inconsequential that the extra height is hardly worth the effort.

Troubleshooting

Ohmmeter readings at the receiver input to the coaxial transmission line should indicate an infinite resistance. A low reading indicates a shorted transmission line, which must be repaired or replaced. Should the antenna not receive properly with a correct resistance reading, the problem is either a break in one of the conductors in the transmission line or an improperly soldered joint at the center insulator. Make certain all connections are solid by securing a good mechanical joint before heat is applied and by using the correct amount of heat to enable the solder to *flow* into the joint.

The inverted-V antenna

When the element sections on each side of the center insulator of a horizontal dipole are dropped significantly, the antenna is called an *inverted-V* (Fig. 7-4). The inverted-V exhibits different characteristics than those associated with true horizontal antenna systems. Both vertical and horizontal radio transmissions are received with equal sensitivity because of the combined vertical and horizontal characteristics of the inverted-V system. One advantage of the inverted-V is that it only needs one large mast or other support. The element ends can be brought to within a few feet of the earth and attached to short wooden ground stakes. The convenience of a coaxial cable feed line is also realized, because the inverted-V exhibits a center impedance of about 50 Ω, which is a good match for RG-58 and RG-8X cable.

7-4 An inverted-V.

The same wire sizes that work for the dipole are also functional for the inverted-V. However, in terms of overall antenna strength, less strain is present on the inverted-V because the element sections are not perfectly horizontal and thus require less mechanical strength. So, if you chose #14 over #16 wire (for example) because of the strength factor for the standard dipole, you can go with the smaller wire for the inverted-V.

The inverted-V has one difference from the standard dipole. The inverted-V is 7% shorter than the dipole because of the electrical effects of the drooping elements.

Installation of the inverted-V is simple—it's even almost fun! Depending on what you plan to use for the center support, there are a variety of ways that the inverted-V can be installed.

- If you are using a house or house attachment as a support, you can either climb a ladder or walk out on a flat roof and attach the center insulator to something sturdy (Figs. 7-4 and 7-5). Then, let the ends droop to the ground. At my parents' house, I can open up the attic window and tie the center insulator to the television antenna mast.
- If the support is a mast that you are building, you can attach the inverted-V to the top with a U-bolt (Fig. 7-6) or even a bent nail. Then, simply raise the mast with the inverted-V attached and allow the ends of the antenna to droop within reaching distance.

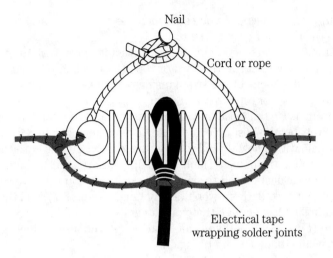

7-5 Holding the center of an inverted-V up against a house.

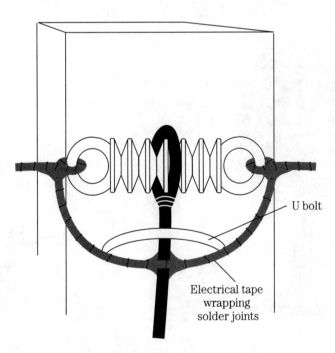

7-6 Holding the center of an inverted-V against a mast with a U bolt.

- If the support is a flagpole, you can attach the center insulator to the rope and run the inverted-V up to the top.
- If the support is a tree limb, you need to do some extra work to get the antenna in place. First run the cord or rope (with which you plan to secure the ends) through one of the strain insulators. Make sure that you have more than enough cord or rope to reach from the ground to the tree limb and back to the ground. Tie the loose end of the rope or cord to a solid, throwable object. Probably the best objects would be a hockey puck or a wooden croquet ball, with a hole drilled through the center. Tie the cord through the hole and around the object. Then, warm up your arm, pick a limb, have enough slack available, and throw! If you are lucky, you will throw over the limb that you picked, there won't be any tangles (Fig. 7-7), and the weight will be dangling low enough that you can grab it and pull the center up to that limb (Fig. 7-8). If not, you can try to "rock" the weight down or you can pull the whole thing out and try again.

I have used this method dozens of times with inverted-Vs. A lot depends on sheer luck. At times, I have gotten the center up to between 45' and 50' and installed the whole thing in 10 minutes. At other times, I have hit the limb that I was aiming for three times in a row, got into countless tangles, and ended up with my weight (usually a rock) stuck up in a tree (sometimes several times). It can be maddening, to say the least!

7-7 Throwing an end weight into a tree.

When you have the center in its proper location, the ends are easy to finish off. Both of the end egg insulators should be attached to a length of support rope or cord. Pull each leg out about 45° away from the vertical length of coaxial cable and spike

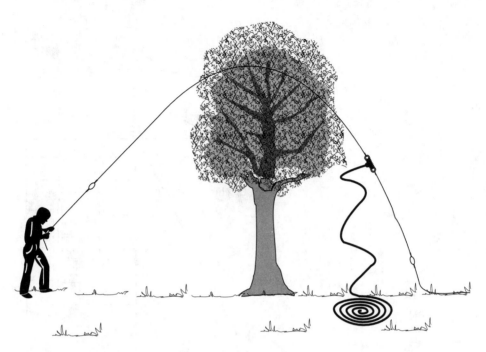

7-8 Pulling an antenna into place.

each end to the ground with a rod, pipe, or stake. The angles that the antenna elements are hung at aren't critical, but it will make a difference in the receiving/transmitting properties of your particular antenna. Another method of tying off the ends is to tie them to tree limbs. I like this method because it keeps the antenna off the ground, where people might trip (or otherwise injure themselves) on it.

The inverted-V antenna is ideal for the shortwave listener who does not have adequate space to erect a basic horizontal antenna system. Loading coils can be used to effectively shorten antenna elements, but full-size antennas always perform better. The inverted-V is a full-sized antenna, and you can expect excellent reception of signals that have been transmitted from horizontally and vertically polarized antennas. By changing the position of the stakes that secure the antenna to the ground, you can change the directional pick-up of the inverted-V to provide optimum reception of signals coming in from a particular area.

The sloper

Some people consider the inverted-V and the sloper to be compensation antennas, that is, dipole arrangements to be installed when a full-length dipole won't fit on a lot. Being a long-time fan of inverted-Vs, I have to disagree. The sloper, like the inverted-V, has its own particular receiving, transmitting, and installation characteristics. The sloper is a standard dipole that has one end attached high up on a building (or other support) and the other staked down near the ground (Fig. 7-9).

The interesting receiving/transmitting characteristic of the sloper is that it is directional from where the lower end of the antenna is pointing. The sloper isn't as di-

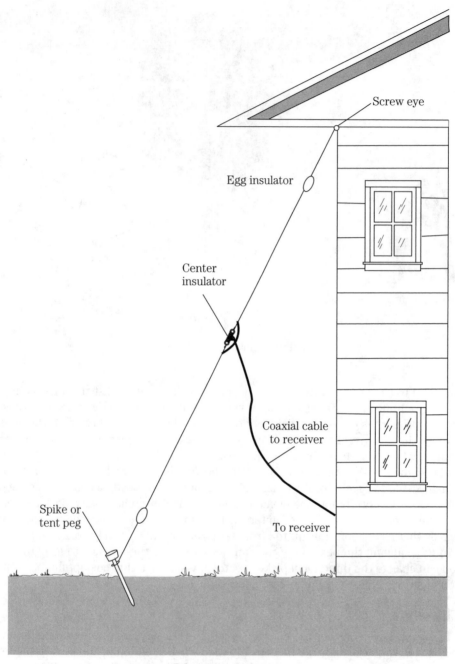

Screw eye

Egg insulator

Center
insulator

Coaxial cable
to receiver

Spike or
tent peg

To receiver

7-9 A sloper antenna.

rectional as many of the antennas that are designed for directional use, but this characteristic can be augmented if you use a metallic mast or support.

To build a sloper, follow the instructions for building the standard dipole antenna. To install a sloper, follow the directions for raising the center of the inverted-V. The big difference is that you only pull one end of the antenna up to the top and that you only have one end to stake to the ground. Like the inverted-V, the angle of the antenna isn't especially critical, but it will affect the receiving/transmitting characteristics of the antenna.

Because of the relatively small amount of space that a sloper requires, some radio hobbyists install four slopers (one in each direction). This arrangement is inexpensive, somewhat directional, easy to build, and only one support is required (Fig. 7-10). These are some real advantages over the very expensive, difficult-to-install yagis, beams, and log periodics.

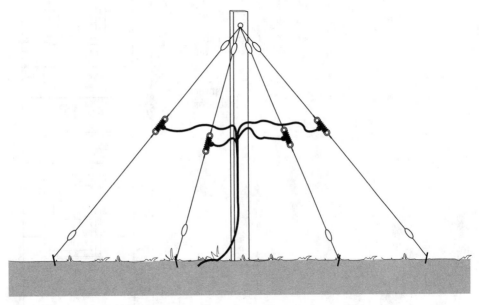

7-10 A system of four slopers mounted on a mast.

The vertical dipole

Vertical dipoles (Fig. 7-11) don't have nearly as many advantages as the sloper or the inverted-V. Most of the advantages that vertical dipoles have are more strategy than performance-oriented. For one, the vertical dipole doesn't require an excellent ground system, like the quarter-wave vertical. Also, the vertical dipole is best run out of a second-story window. These two characteristics make the vertical dipole perfect for apartment dwellers—especially second-story apartment renters.

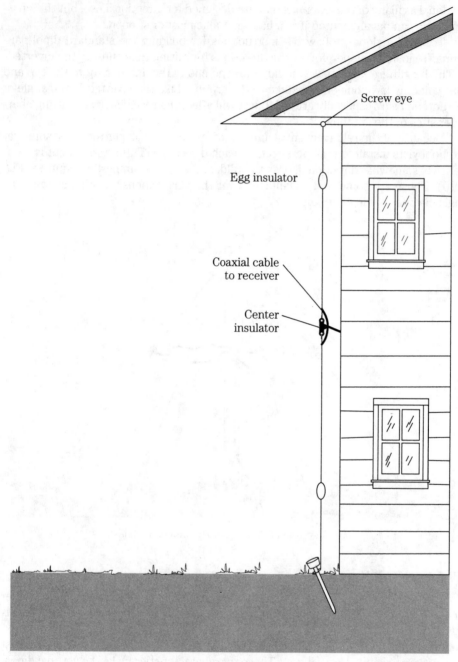

Screw eye

Egg insulator

Coaxial cable
to receiver

Center
insulator

7-11 A vertical dipole.

If the top of the dipole can be installed under the eaves of the house, it will perform well under many conditions. However, the one condition that will severely hamper the performance of the vertical dipole is if it is installed under the eaves of the roof and the house is sided with aluminum. Aluminum siding shields much of the antenna and results in clear reception from only one direction. Transmitting-wise, much of the signal would be absorbed, and thus wasted, by the aluminum siding.

From a second-story location, the run of coaxial cable to the antenna could be as little as 5' or 6', and that could put the price of a vertical dipole at less than $10. This low cost, and the low profile of the vertical dipole, make it possibly the cheapest and the best-hidden variation of the standard dipole antenna. Some literature suggests that the vertical dipole makes an excellent antenna to hide within a PVC pipe for use as a secret transmitting flagpole. I disagree because the coaxial cable still needs to feed into the center of the PVC pipe. Unless your faux flagpole is right against the side of your house (a lousy place for a flagpole because the flag will be hidden and will be thrashed against your house), the coax will probably run out from the center of the flagpole at least 15' to your window. As a result, this antenna will hardly be a secret transmitting source. Try a quarter-wave dipole for that.

For building the vertical dipole, follow the same procedures that were used to construct the standard dipole antenna. You can install the vertical dipole by climbing a ladder to the eaves of the house, attaching a screw eye into solid wood, and knotting a cord or rope between the end egg insulator and the screw eye. Then the other end of the dipole can be staked to the ground. Either the mast-raising method or the tree-raising method can also be used (see the section on raising the inverted-V).

The multiband cage dipole

One interesting dipole variation that is often considered to be a separate form of antenna is the *multiband dipole* (Fig. 7-12). The multiband dipole has been configured in many different forms over the years, but in this case, I'm discussing the cage-style dipole instead because it is easier to install than other types of multiband antennas and it is cheaper to build (fewer egg strain insulators) than the other common type of multiband dipole.

The multiband cage dipole requires a bit more work, but it will probably be worth it to you. The extra work for the cage dipole is put into cutting and drilling spacers to go down the length of the antenna. Normally, the elements of the standard cage dipole are all either the same length or slightly different lengths. The longest element of the antenna is cut for the lowest frequency of the band and the shortest element is cut for the frequency at the top of the band. The slightly different lengths make the antenna resonate throughout an entire frequency band rather than just at one frequency. As a result, this antenna requires the same amount of space as a regular dipole antenna, yet it is more effective over a wider range of frequencies.

If you are interested in a wideband dipole, try the cage dipole with slightly variable lengths. To tell you the truth, although I had seen the cage dipole in various an-

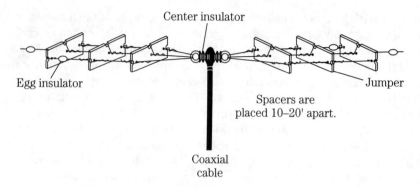

Center insulator

Egg insulator

Jumper

Spacers are
placed 10–20' apart.

Coaxial
cable

7-12 A three-band version of the multiband cage dipole.

tenna articles and books in the past, the multiband version is something that I thought of and included in this book. As a result, it has not been thoroughly tested, like most of the other antennas in this book. Neither the basic idea nor the fact that the antenna hasn't been thoroughly tested are significant. Multiband dipoles have been around for years; the only real difference here is the manner in which the antenna elements are held apart. This antenna performs well for receiving, but I'm not sure how it works for transmitting, with the wires so close together. I am neither a licensed radio amateur nor a CBer; I was unable to test this antenna for transmitting.

The multiband cage dipole can be built in nearly the same way as the traditional dipole (see the instructions for building the standard dipole antenna). However, each side of the multiband dipole consists of several elements. Also, because of the jumpers, which help secure the wire elements to the spreaders, you should use uninsulated copper or copper-clad wire. Group the elements needed for each side together, twist them around the center conductor (for the one side) and the shielded braid (for the other side) of the coaxial cable, then solder the large joint carefully.

You can cut the spreaders out of almost any solid insulator, but I would guess that thick Plexiglas is the least expensive and most common suitable material. The shape of the spacers depends on the number of wires that you attach to each side. Of course, the number of bands that you want to cover with this antenna determines the number of wires that you install in it.

I imagine that the three favorite types of multiband cage dipole would be those with three, four, or five elements (Fig. 7-13). The spacer arrangements for this number of antenna elements are rather simple to design. The three-element version can be designed with all three elements in a row in a long, thin spacer. For the four-element version, the spacer is in the shape of a triangle; one wire runs through each tip of the triangle, and one wire runs through the center of each triangle. The five-element version is very similar to the four-element version; the spacer is in the shape of a square, with one wire running through each tip, and one running through the center. In order for this system to be mechanically stable, the longest antenna element must run through the center of the spacer in all cases.

The number of spacers that you should use per side depends on the number of elements that you use and also on the length of the antennas. A spacer should be

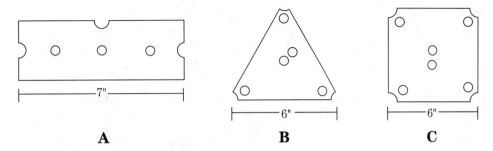

7-13 Spacers: A) three element, B) four element, and C) five element.

placed at the end of each element (except for the last element, which has a strain insulator at the end), and a spacer should be installed about every 10' to 20' to keep the wires separate. For example, a 10-/11-/13-meter multiband requires fewer spacers than a 120-/90-/75-/60-/48-meter version.

Cut out all of the spacers with a hacksaw. Once you have finished, cut ¼" deep grooves into the corners (if the spacers are triangular or squared) or into the one side (if the spacers are long rectangles for the three-element version). These grooves are slots for jumper wires to fit in and hold the antenna elements taut (Fig. 7-14). Then, drill small holes (a ⅛" bit should work fine) about ½" in from the back edge of each groove. For the triangular and squared spacers, also drill one hole in the center and another hole ½" from that hole. The hole in the center is where the longest element will run and the other hole is for the jumper to hold the spacer in position.

Normally, I prefer insulated wire to uninsulated stranded wire because the slick rubber slides over tree limbs and other objects much better than stranded wire. In this case, because of the jumpers that must be soldered in place, the uninsulated variety is much more practical. Measure and cut the element wires and coaxial cable as you would for a standard dipole antenna. The difference here is that several elements must be soldered to the center conductor and the shielded braid (respectively) of the coaxial cable. Twist these conductors together and make a solid physical joint, then solder each joint.

Then, spread the antenna out on a floor and string the spacers down the wire. Make sure that the longest element runs through the center of the spacers. The first spacer should be placed very close to the solder joint at the center of the antenna. Then, cut enough 4" wire "jumpers" to jump each element on the spacer. Twist each jumper around the element on one side of the spacer, run it through the groove, and twist it around the element on the other side of the spacer. Then, solder each twisted joint (Fig. 7-14). Where you place the next joint is up to you (unless the end of one of the wire elements is less than 15' away). When you install the next spacer, make sure that the elements are all fairly tight and that the spacer is straight. Otherwise, one or more of the elements will sag and possibly cause installation problems or an electrical short. As stated earlier, the average distance between spacers should be about 10' to 20', although this distance can vary depending on your personal preferences.

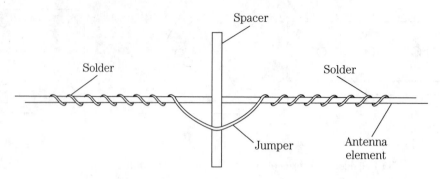

7-14 A close-up of a spacer jumper.

Depending on your techniques, you need to treat the spacer at the end of an element a bit differently than the regular spacers. The best method is to place the spacer about 7" away from the end of the antenna element, attach all of the jumpers, then add an egg insulator at the end of the wire. Add thin cord to run through the egg insulator to the last spacer. Without the cord, the antenna will hang off balance. If you are a shortwave listener (not an amateur operator) and you want to skip the egg insulator, loop the end of the antenna back through the groove and twist it around itself on the other side of the spacer. Make sure that you leave enough of a loop to tie the end cord through. Then solder the loop joint. Personally, I would advise against this method and stick with the egg insulators; they provide a much more solid connection.

Continue this process of adding spacers until you reach the spacer at the end of the next-to-last antenna element. At this spacer, run the next-to-last element (you should be at its end) through the hole, back through the groove, twist it back on itself, then solder the joint (Fig. 7-15). Use the same technique to end the cords at this spacer (except, of course, don't solder the cords!). At this point, the wire in the center spacer should be the only element still running. Attach an egg strain insulator to the end of this element.

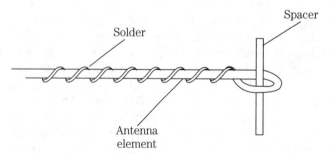

7-15 A close-up of the spacer for the next-to-last antenna element.

As stated at the beginning of this section, the multiband cage dipole is a real space saver. One problem that you might have with installing it is that you can't really run it through trees, like you can with standard dipoles. As complicated as the wiring is, you should try to take any precautions to avoid tangles and knots. Like the dipole, the multiband cage dipole can be installed as a dipole, inverted-V, sloper, or vertical dipole. Also, it can be installed using the same methods you would for those antennas (see the methods of installation in the inverted-V section). The one way that absolutely will not work is the method where one element is thrown over a branch and the center of the coax is pulled to the top of the limb. If you try this method, the antenna will probably become lodged in the tree and break a few solder joints.

Twin-lead dipole antenna

The *twin-lead dipole antenna* (Fig. 7-16) is constructed entirely of standard 300-Ω television hook-up wire (often referred to as *twin-lead cable* because it is constructed with two discrete conductors that are separated and insulated by a high-grade flexible plastic). Any store that carries television parts and accessories will have this type of cable in great quantity and at reasonable prices. Only consider the exterior-grade varieties for antenna construction use. The major advantages of twin-lead dipole antennas are that they are very inexpensive and easy to build.

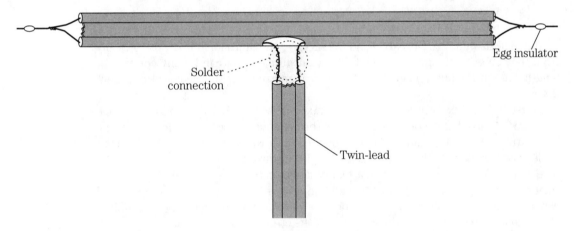

Solder connection

Egg insulator

Twin-lead

7-16 A twin-lead dipole.

The twin-lead dipole is fine for both receiving and transmitting. However, if you want to use it for transmitting, you must use a transmatch between your transmitter and the antenna. You can feed it with coaxial cable, but you must use a 4:1 balun (Fig. 7-17), such as the B4-1.K (available from the Radio Works Inc., P.O. Box 6159, Portsmouth, VA 23703, for $22.95). If you don't own a transmatch and if the low-cost factor was one of the reasons that interested you in the twin-lead dipole, forget it. The variations of the standard dipole are cheaper to build.

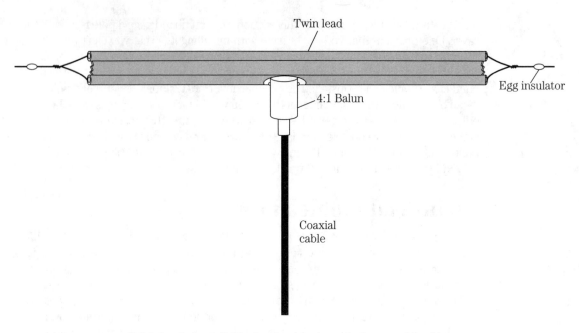

7-17 A twin-lead dipole that has been matched to coaxial cable.

The television cable dipole is constructed in two parts. The main element is mounted horizontally to the earth, and the receiver transmission line drops vertically from the center of the main element. The transmission line can be any convenient length, but cut the antenna element to the proper size by using the chart in Appendix A.

First, roll out the twin-lead on the ground or on some other flat working surface. Measure the cable to the correct length from the chart and allow 2' extra for any errors. This extra cable can be trimmed later if you are not satisfied with this length. Fold the cable exactly in half. At this point, make a single cut through one, and only one, of the wire conductors that lie under the plastic insulation on the outside edges. Trim the insulation from the severed conductor for 2" on each side. Avoid nicking the exposed wires, which you will later connect to the receiver transmission line. Notice that only one conductor, or one side, of the cable is cut; the other side remains intact.

Unfold the cable and strip all of the insulation from both ends for a distance of 1'. This is best accomplished by exposing each conductor with a knife and pulling the conductors away from the plastic. Cut the center portion of the insulation at the base of the exposed wires. Twist the exposed conductors together for their full lengths at both ends and make solder connections at the points closest to the intact insulation. The exposed, twisted conductors at each end will be connected to the support insulators during a later construction step. Remeasure the insulated portion of the antenna element; the total length should be as specified in the antenna element chart in Appendix A.

Next, install the transmission line from the operating position at the receiver to the base of the antenna site. An adequate amount of twin-lead should be allotted to reach the center of the antenna when it is permanently mounted. Any extra cable can be cut to proper length after the antenna is erected. Use any available supports for the cable, such as the side of a house or trees standing along the transmission-line route. When the end of the line reaches the antenna mounting site, strip the insulation from both sides of the cable for 2", exposing both conductors. Bring the antenna element into position on the ground below the mounting site and twist the conductors at its center around the wires at the end of the receiver transmission line. The left conductor of the element goes to one conductor of the transmission line, the right conductor of the element to the other. Solder the connections and insulate them from each other by wrapping each twisted conductor with high-quality electrical tape.

The third step is to connect the ends of the antenna elements to the ceramic insulators. Run each end through one eye of an insulator and wrap the wire back around itself for the entire length available, then solder the joints. Tape all exposed wire with electrical tape to add mechanical strength and to protect against weather conditions.

All antenna connections are now complete, but go back over each step to ensure proper connections at all points. Look for any nicks or breaks in all conductors. Considering the strength of the twin-lead's jacket, you probably would have to hit it with a hatchet to break the conductors! Regardless, any breaks can be repaired by soldering and taping.

Now, feed nylon clothesline rope through the remaining eye in each insulator and securely tie it. Connect the other ends to the antenna supports and hoist one end at a time into the mounting position. The receiver feed line can be adjusted at this point so that a condition of too much or too little slack does not exist.

If you are using this antenna for transmitting, use standard 300-Ω twin-lead insulators every 6' or so along the line to ensure proper spacing from surrounding objects. Twin-lead cable should never be allowed to lie against any object, because the antenna efficiency will be decreased. If you are only using this antenna for receiving, you can use it with or without the insulators. You might choose to go with the insulators anyway, to keep the twin-lead from drooping.

The final step is to bare the two conductors at the receiver end of the transmission line and make the proper connections. The antenna trim control on the receiver (if your receiver has one of these controls) can be adjusted for peak reception and the frequencies the antenna was designed for should be coming in clearly.

Troubleshooting

The twin-lead antenna is so simple in design that any failure in performance can be attributed to broken conductors or two conductors that have shorted together. An ohmmeter should read a resistance of less than 10 Ω when connected across the receiver transmission line input. Very long transmission lines might read a little higher. An indication of very high or infinite resistance reveals a break at some point in the transmission line or antenna element. If you can't find the trouble by taking these measurements, you'll need to lower the antenna and disconnect the feed line. Once the antenna is down, it will probably be much easier to "eyeball" the antenna for the problem than to locate it by taking electronic tests.

With the conductors at each end of the line insulated from each other, the ohm-meter should read infinite resistance when the probes are placed across the wires at one end. When the wires at the other end are wrapped together, the ohmmeter should read very low resistance. Any other indications mean a faulty feed line that should be replaced. When the probes are placed across the two conductors at the center of the antenna element, a very low resistance should be read. Any reading of high resistance indicates a broken conductor in the element, which should also be repaired or replaced.

The quarter-wave vertical

The *quarter-wave vertical* isn't quite as popular as the dipole, but it certainly ranks high with the other classic radio antennas. The way I see it, in order to qualify as a true classic radio antenna, an antenna must not only be popular, but it must be the foundation upon which other popular antennas are built.

A quarter-wave vertical is like a vertical half-wave dipole in some ways. Both use a quarter-wave element for the "hot" side and both are fed with coaxial cable. The difference is that, instead of using another quarter-wave antenna element connected to the braid side of the coaxial cable, the quarter-wave vertical has the braid connected to ground. This arrangement, with the braid connected to ground and the center conductor connected to the antenna element, is critical. Because of this, the braided side of the dipole is sometimes called the *ground element* and the side that is connected to the center conductor is sometimes called the *hot element*.

As you probably suspected by now, the quarter-wave vertical is constructed similar to the dipole, except with a good ground system replacing the ground element. The better the ground, the better the quarter-wave vertical will perform—especially when transmitting. For best performance, follow the instructions for installing a ground system in chapter 6.

All of that sounds simple enough, but here is where the fun comes in. Because the quarter-wave vertical uses a single vertical element, most people don't use wire for that element; they use a rigid conductor. Of course, you can use a wire element if you want to—it can be hung from a tree, from a PVC or wooden mast, or from the eaves of your house (see the inverted-V section for some general installation tips). In this setting, it is perfect for the hobbyist who is living in a neighborhood or planned community where outside antennas are not permissible. It is very difficult to see along the side of a house and it would be impossible to see inside a PVC flagpole. The wire-element version of the quarter-wave vertical is one of the best hidden antennas available.

The rigid conductor is made out of aluminum tubing, held in place with some sort of lower support at the bottom and with guy wires at the top. Because the rigid support is especially useful where towers and masts are difficult to install, some people use quarter-wave verticals on the house roof. In this arrangement, the vertical element can be built onto a wooden mount, or it can be attached to a television antenna roof mount, so long as it is insulated from the metal mount. Of course, the first question is "what about the ground?" Some people lay out the ground radials on the roof. But this makes your house a very attractive target for lightning, so I don't recommend this sort of installation. Also, the side effects of having the ground radials lying on the roof could be curious for transmitting: Do the light bulbs upstairs all mysteriously glow while you transmit, and do squirrels suddenly drop dead on your roof while you transmit in the rain?

A better, safer version of the quarter-wave vertical with a rigid vertical element would be on the side of a wooden fence post (Fig. 7-18). Of course, most people who want to use a quarter-wave vertical are limited by space, which means that they are probably living on a city or suburban lot. This being the case, it is doubtful that any fields or ranches are fenced off in your backyard. So, you have to trek down to the local hardware supply store, purchase a wooden fence post, and dig a hole for it.

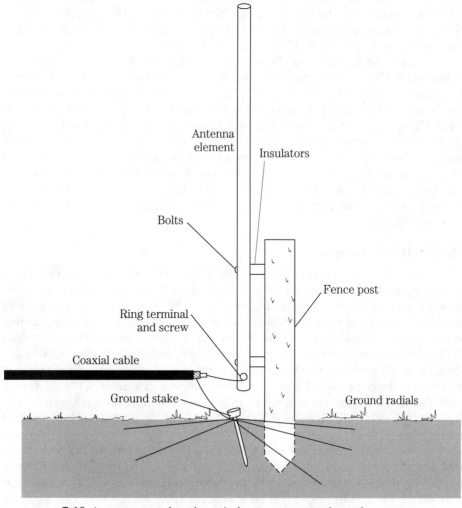

7-18 A quarter-wavelength vertical antenna mounted on a fence post.

Because wood is a moderately good insulator and wet or damp wood isn't, you should apply paint or polyurethane to the fence post to keep it from grounding the vertical element. This step is especially important if you will be bolting the element directly to the fence post. This procedure works, but I would rather add an insulator between the fence post and the antenna element. My automatic insulator choice for this situation is a piece of tire rubber. Just make sure that you don't use pieces that contain steel belts or you could have some real problems trying to drill bolt holes through the rubber.

First, install the fence post if you haven't done so already. You should have bolts that are long enough to reach all the way through the antenna element, through the insulator (if you decide to use one), and through the fence post . . . with enough left over for a nut to screw on the end. Then, you must drill two holes through the element—one about 2" from the bottom of the tubing and one that aligns near the top of the fence post. Drill an additional smaller hole 1" up from the bottom of the tubing, and 90° away from the other holes. This hole is where the center conductor of the coaxial cable should be bolted in place. Next, drill holes through the insulators. Place the tubing against the fence post and use a pencil to mark through the holes where you plan to drill. Then drill the holes in the fence post.

If the antenna is more than about 15' tall, use guy wires. Follow the directions for guying the PVC tower in chapter 5. The element should be guyed, not just to protect people and property against destruction, but to protect your antenna. Bolt the tubing tight, but be sure that you don't tighten the bolts so much that the tubing bends. Otherwise, the tubing would probably buckle in the first stiff wind.

Follow the instructions for preparing the coaxial cable for the dipole antenna (earlier in this chapter). The only difference is that you should solder a noninsulated ring terminal to the end of the center conductor of the coaxial cable and solder the braid to the ground clamp. Then, bolt the ring terminal to the hole in the antenna element. This connection must be tight or it will corrode slightly and the antenna will be very inefficient.

The multiband vertical

The *multiband vertical antenna* (Fig. 7-19) has the same relationship to a quarter-wave vertical antenna that a multiband dipole has to a standard dipole. Like the multiband dipole, the multiband vertical is the same as the antenna that it was named for, except that it has extra elements. With these extra elements, the antenna provides frequency coverage for more bands than a single element antenna covers.

Unlike many quarter-wave verticals, the multiband vertical always uses wire antenna elements. It wouldn't be practical to mount several aluminum tubing elements at various nonvertical angles. Instead, the wire elements are soldered to the center conductor of the coaxial cable and they radiate out from this point. Otherwise, the same construction techniques used for the wire version of the quarter-wave vertical can be followed for this antenna.

The real working difference with this antenna is how it is mounted. Two of the best mounting methods for this antenna are either with the elements all hanging from a horizontally suspended rope or attached to the side of a house. The multiband vertical that I built was suspended on a diagonal rope using a very fine gauge of enamelled wire. Spacing the elements while still keeping them all taut, can be tricky.

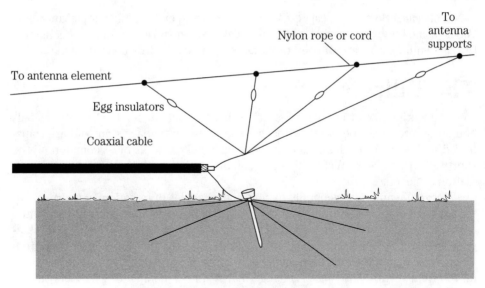

7-19 A multiband wire vertical antenna.

I completed the antenna, took it outside, and connected it to the ground. I threw kite string over a tree limb using the standard "baseball toss method" (see the section on raising inverted-V antennas). Then, I organized the antenna elements from longest to shortest and guessed where they should be placed on the string. After I tied the elements to the string, I attached the other end of the string to the house and I started to pull the entire configuration into the air. I had to occasionally stop to sort out the tangled elements, but otherwise, it went up easily.

The can vertical

Some other variations of the quarter-wave vertical also exist. My favorite (you might have noticed by now that my favorites are some of the strangest antennas) is the "beer can vertical," which has been covered by several magazines in the past. However, the first time that I believe that the idea was put into print was in 1955 in *QST*. The whole concept behind the beer can vertical was to construct the vertical element (usually aluminum tubing or wire in this book) out of the proper length of beer cans. These cans were all soldered together and coated with silver spray paint. The top of the top can was cut off and the whole element was turned upside-down and placed on a pop bottle, which insulated the vertical element from the ground. Otherwise, the antenna used guy wires for support, rather than depend on the fragile solder joints, and the antenna mast was not braced against a fence post for extra support (although it could be).

Back in 1955, all beverage cans were steel and had a wide seam down the side, which provided extra support. Today, these cans are aluminum, and beer cans seem to be constructed out of the lightest material possible. As a result, these cans would be very difficult to solder and they would probably collapse at the first sneeze. Currently, I think that the best bets for building a can vertical would be soup, fruit, or vegetable cans. Soup cans, especially, fit well over the ends of large applesauce jars. Maybe some hobbyists would feel less motivated to finish 74 cans of lima beans than the same number of cans of beer, but that's the price of sturdy construction.

The T dipole antenna

As mentioned in the "Basics" section in the front of this book, some signals bounce several times before they reach a shortwave antenna system and are transferred to the receiver. This phenomenon is called *skip* and is most common on the shortwave frequencies. When skip occurs, a distortion or altering of the angle of radiation can occur.

Horizontal antennas generally exhibit higher angles of radiation and vertical antennas have lower radiation angles. A signal that was originally transmitted from a horizontal antenna with a high angle of radiation might be changed through the skipping process to exhibit a low angle of radiation—as though it was transmitted from an antenna with a low radiation angle. The same is true of signals originally transmitted from vertical antennas. A change that results in complete reversal of the radiation angle is not often the case, but combinations of high and low angles of radiation are very common.

The *T antenna* is sensitive to both high and low angles of signal radiation and has the advantage of responding sensitively to radio signals of many different characteristics. The T antenna provides very satisfactory operation for signals exhibiting high or low angles of radiation and everything in between.

A basic horizontal dipole antenna and a basic vertical dipole antenna are combined to form the T system (Fig. 7-20). Both elements are fed at their centers with a coaxial cable transmission line. The vertical dipole support (mast) can be used to provide support for the center of the large dipole element when the system is designed for the lower frequencies, which require sizable lengths of wire to operate properly.

Determine element length from the chart in Appendix A, which you can use to compute the correct dimensions of both the vertical and the horizontal portions of the T antenna. It is possible to alter the designs slightly by cutting the vertical element for one frequency and the horizontal element for another. This results in multifrequency coverage with one antenna system. As mentioned before, when a broad range of signals is to be covered, cut the element lengths to the dimensions required to cover the lowest frequency likely to be received. The T antenna still does a good job of receiving the other frequencies.

Begin construction by measuring the correct lengths of wire as determined by the element chart in Appendix A. This chart shows the correct lengths for the entire element, which must be cut at the halfway point. When this is done, you should have four individual lengths of wire. Always allow 1' extra of element for connection to the ceramic insulators at the center and end. If insulated copper wire is used for each antenna element, it should be stripped bare for a length of 3" on every end.

Arrange the sections of antenna elements on your working area in positions similar to where each will be when the antenna system is erected. Place the center insulator at the point where the elements were cut and thread one end of the

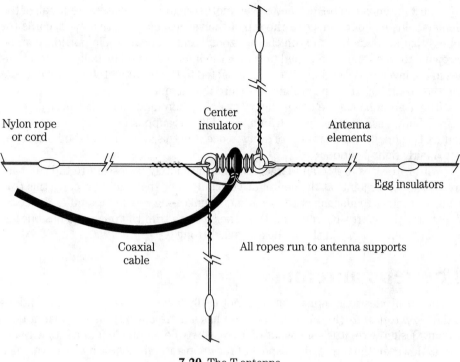

Nylon rope or cord

Center insulator

Antenna elements

Egg insulators

Coaxial cable

All ropes run to antenna supports

7-20 The T antenna.

horizontal and one end of the vertical element through one side. Do the same with the remaining portions of the horizontal and vertical elements on the opposite end of the center insulator. Now, strip about 6" of insulation from the coaxial cable at the antenna connection end. Feed the separated center and outer conductors through the same insulator eyes as the ends of the two antenna elements. Secure the conductors and element ends to the insulator by wrapping them back on themselves, then solder all three wires in each insulator eye. Be certain that you have a strong mechanical connection before you solder the joint. Now, connect the remaining insulators to the ends of the antenna elements. Then, attach the support ropes through the remaining insulator eyes.

The installation of the T antenna can be a bit tedious with four elements having to be strung up in different directions, but there are several different methods you can use. If the vertical dipole will be mounted on a mast, it is best for the top of the vertical dipole to be attached to the top of the mast before it is raised. Then, when the mast is raised, half of the elements will already be installed. Afterwards, the horizontal dipole portion (the other two elements) can be set up just like a common dipole (see the installation techniques for the inverted-V).

One possibility for the T antenna would be to make a hybrid version. The vertical dipole portion of the T could be made out of metal tubing and the horizontal dipole out of wire. This version of the T can be installed in the same manner as the version in the previous paragraphs.

The T antenna can be installed in yet another manner by using wire for all of the elements. Instead of connecting the top of the vertical element to a mast, cords (or ropes) that are attached to both the horizontal and vertical dipole portions can be thrown into trees and then pulled taut (see the information on installing wire antennas in the inverted-V section). A cord connected to the bottom of the vertical dipole can then be staked into the ground to secure the element.

The T antenna can be a very heavy system when long element lengths are required, but it has a mechanical advantage in that it is supported at its ends and at its center. Do not allow a great deal of sway to occur in this system. Pull the hoist ropes into a fairly tight position.

With wire sizes of #14 and larger, it is not absolutely necessary to tape all bare areas. The solder joints at the center are the only ones that should receive this covering, to protect them against the weather. Connect the remaining end of the coaxial cable to the shortwave receiver. Peak the antenna trim (if your radio has one) as described before and you should hear signals strongly.

The zepp antenna

One truly classic antenna that does not really have a whole family of variations is the *zepp antenna* (Fig. 7-21). The zepp has a more curious history than it does design. Design-wise, it is somewhat of a cross between a dipole and a longwire antenna. However, the interesting aspect of the zepp antenna is how it was developed. As you might have expected, *zepp* is short for *zeppelin*. Dirigibles were at the forefront of airflight in the early 1900s. Before the tragic crash of the *Hindenburg* in 1937, it appeared that dirigibles might be the new force in air transportation. Of course, public and commercial transportation requires some sort of reliable communications system. Radio was chosen as the best system, but installing an antenna on a blimp became a problem.

The system that was chosen for the zeppelins was an end-fed single-element antenna. This antenna was perfect because it required no support points for the antenna element to be mounted—it only needed to hang from the underside of the dirigible. The zepp antenna was a perfect system for the dirigible, but it couldn't save lighter-than-aircraft. After the famous crashes of the *Shenandoah* and the *Hindenburg*, dirigibles faded from view, except for a few well-known novelties, such as the Goodyear line of blimps.

Zepp antennas were very popular in the 1930s, but over the past 40 years, they too have almost totally faded from view. Today, zepp antennas are rarely used, but they are interesting and amazingly simple antennas. One of the problems with using zepp antennas for shortwave listening is that they are fed with 450- or 600-Ω ladder transmission line. In order to use this sort of transmission line effectively, you must have an antenna tuner. Many amateur radio operators have antenna tuners, but so many antennas work well for shortwave listening that it's better to pick a different antenna than to buy an antenna tuner just to match one particular type of antenna.

For amateur radio use, zepp antennas are more practical, but they still have some drawbacks. They are somewhat directional off the far end of the antenna element. This can work to the advantage or disadvantage of an operator, depending on

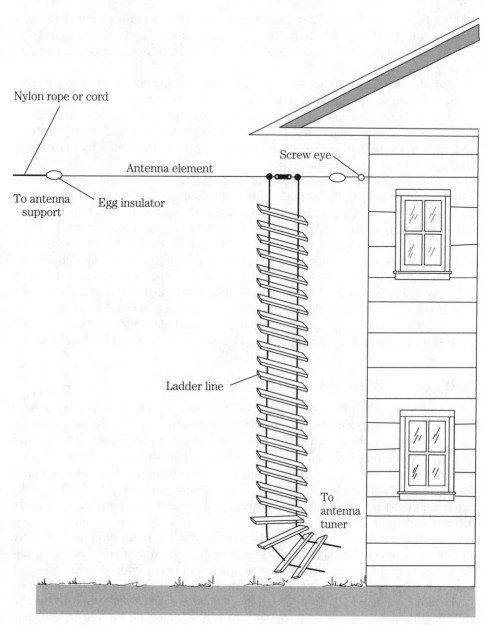

Nylon rope or cord

Antenna element

Screw eye

To antenna
support

Egg insulator

Ladder line

To
antenna
tuner

7-21 The zepp antenna.

what type of coverage the operator wants. One of the worst problems with zepp antennas occurs when transmitting. I have been trying to avoid heavy antenna theory throughout this book, however, antennas have high and low voltage and high and low current points (for transmitting) across them. The antenna works fine if it is used at an odd multiple of the half-wave length. For example, it works well at ½, ¾, 2½ (etc.)

wavelength. But, if the antenna is used at an even length, the transmission line feeds in at a high-voltage point. When that happens, much power is reflected back into the radio and the "shack." Not only is power wasted, but it can cause electrical shocks at the equipment. Nasty!

The zepp antenna is about as easy to construct as any antenna that is effective for both shortwave listening and transmitting. Simply cut a half-wavelength piece of wire for the antenna element, and cut an appropriately long piece of ladder line. Strip about 4" of insulation from the wire of one side of the transmission line, then twist the wires together and solder them. Make sure that the solder flows throughout the joint and that it is solid.

Nothing is attached to the other element of the ladder line. The unconnected side of the ladder line is connected at the bottom to the ground side of the transmitter or antenna tuner. The side of the transmission line that is connected to the antenna element at the top is connected to the "hot" side of the transmitter or antenna tuner.

Installing the zepp is easy. Tie a short length of rope or cord to the top of the ladder transmission line. Tie the other side of the rope or cord to the house through a screw eye attached to the house. Make sure that you attach the screw eye into a solid piece (solid wood, not vinyl siding, for example) of the house so that it will not pull out when large stresses are placed on the antenna. Attach the other end to a securing rope or cord. This securing rope or cord should then be supported on a mast or in a tree (see the instructions for stringing up antennas under the inverted-V section in this chapter).

Single-element loop antennas

Loop antennas are interesting in that only one antenna element is used and both sides of the transmission line are connected to the opposite ends of the same element. The result is a somewhat directional antenna. Very often loop antennas are only considered to be small coils of wire on a box or ferrite form that have very directional characteristics. A common example of these multiturn receiving antennas are the ferrite loop antennas that are built inside any common AM (mediumwave) radio. Because these receiving loop antennas are extremely directional, they are covered in chapter 10.

Both of the loop antennas in this chapter are amateur radio antennas—suitable for both receiving and transmitting. The quad antenna is almost never used in a single-element configuration—it's usually mounted within an array with several other nearly identical elements on a rotatable beam. This typical quad configuration is covered further in chapter 10. Even though the delta loop is just a slight variation on the quad, it is normally used in a single-element configuration for most shortwave frequencies and not on a rotatable beam.

The single-element quad antenna

The *single-element quad antenna* derives its name from its four sides and from the single element, which is one wavelength at the operating design frequency (Fig. 7-22). This system is fed with 52-Ω coaxial cable, which is connected at a point only a foot or so from the ground. Unfortunately, in order to properly transmit into a

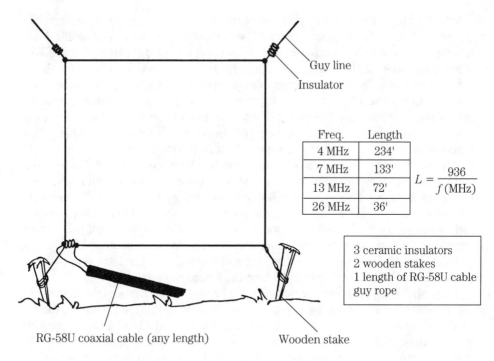

Freq.	Length
4 MHz	234'
7 MHz	133'
13 MHz	72'
26 MHz	36'

$$L = \frac{936}{f \text{ (MHz)}}$$

3 ceramic insulators
2 wooden stakes
1 length of RG-58U cable
guy rope

Guy line
Insulator

RG-58U coaxial cable (any length)   Wooden stake

7-22 The single-element quad antenna.

single-element quad loop, you must use a matching section. This matching section varies in length, depending on the frequency used. Matching sections are based on complicated methods and are beyond the scope of this book.

The receiver transmission line connection to the antenna is the only point where solder connections are required and can be tested for any problems without the necessity of lowering the entire assembly. The main receiving element is situated in both a horizontal and vertical configuration at different points along its length, and it does an admirable job of receiving shortwave signals that are vertically or horizontally polarized.

Begin construction by measuring the correct length of wire from the chart in Fig. 7-22. This is best accomplished by measuring out only ¼ of the required length from the spool of wire, then doubling that length back onto the remaining wire three times. Each side of the box antenna is equal to ¼ of the entire length, so measuring the wire with this method results in bends in the wire at the four points where the supports are to be connected.

Now, prepare the ceramic insulators by slipping the nylon clothesline rope through one eye of each and tying each securely. #14 wire can be used in place of this rope, but in addition to the increased cost, raising and lowering the antenna system will be more difficult because of the added weight and smaller diameter. Now, slip the vacant eye of the two insulators over each end of the antenna bend. Wrap another small piece of wire tightly around the antenna element wire at the points on each side of the ceramic insulators to provide a firm connection that will not slip when the system is raised into position.

With steady pressure, raise each side of the antenna to the correct position. The top portion of the antenna element should be as close to horizontal as possible. Make any adjustments at this point by raising or lowering one of the support ropes. With the bottom portion of the element completely off the ground, the two vertical portions will automatically position themselves perpendicular to the upper element. Position the stakes slightly to one side of these vertical portions of the antenna and drive them into the ground. Tie one end of a short length of nylon clothesline rope to the lower corner of the antenna opposite the corner where the coaxial cable will be connected. Tie the other end of this rope loosely to the stake.

Bare each end of the antenna element wire for a length of about 5". Push each of the uninsulated wires through opposite ends of a ceramic insulator and wrap each back on itself. Leave 1" of wire protruding from each end in order to connect the transmission line. Strip the insulation from 6" of the coaxial cable and separate the braid and inner conductor. Slip the inner conductor through one end of the ceramic insulator and wrap it with the protruding length of the antenna element. The twisted braid should be fed through the other end and twisted with the bare tip of the antenna element. Solder both connections and trim away any excess wire.

There should be sufficient space remaining between the wires and the ceramic insulator to slip another short length of nylon rope through and tie it off securely. You can now tie the other end of the rope to the remaining stake and adjust it for proper horizontal positioning of the bottom element sections. This rope should preferably be fed through the insulator end where the braided portion of the coaxial was connected.

The full-wavelength delta antenna

The *delta loop* (Fig. 7-23) is a very popular amateur radio antenna that hasn't quite caught on with shortwave listeners. This loop, like others, is directional. However, unlike slopers and inverted-Vs, which are also directional, the delta loops are inconvenient to install. An entire switchable array of slopers or inverted-Vs that can receive in all directions can be installed on one support. On the other hand, an array of two delta loops would require at least four supports. Personally, I think the single-element delta and quad loops aren't worth the trouble for shortwave listeners.

The delta loop is normally configured so that the top wire is horizontal and the other two wires meet in a point at the bottom. If it is fed with transmission line at the bottom point, the loop will receive and transmit with horizontal polarization. If it is fed on either one of the downward sloping sides, the polarization will be diagonal—halfway between horizontal and vertical. For some odd reason, delta loops are commonly sold commercially—perhaps it is because they are often fed with coaxial cable and matched with a 4:1 balun. Even so, you can save some money and learn more about radio and electronics by building it yourself.

An antenna system will exhibit a trend toward equal sensitivity in the reception of signals that are being transmitted from vertical and horizontal antennas if large portions of the main element are placed in vertical and horizontal positions. The single-element quad antenna construction project described earlier in this section was composed of one long element that was shaped like a square. This type of antenna performs well, but mounting it can cause problems because of the support and space requirements. The full-wavelength delta antenna is very similar to the single-ele-

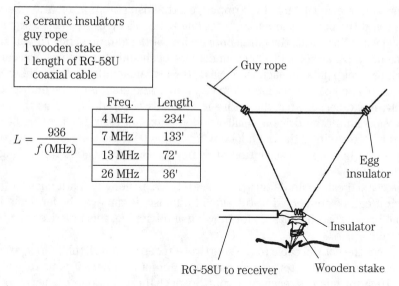

3 ceramic insulators
guy rope
1 wooden stake
1 length of RG-58U
   coaxial cable

$$L = \frac{936}{f\,(MHz)}$$

Freq.	Length
4 MHz	234'
7 MHz	133'
13 MHz	72'
26 MHz	36'

Guy rope

Egg
insulator

Insulator

RG-58U to receiver   Wooden stake

7-23 The delta antenna.

ment quad antenna, but there are only three element portions. Because of the different angles that this antenna element is shaped in, the delta loop responds favorably to signals that have been transmitted from a great variety of antenna types with greatly varying angles of radiation. It requires three mounting points, one of which is a wooden ground stake at the center of the entire assembly.

Measure the wire to correct proportions, as determined by the chart in Fig. 7-23, with an extra allowance of 1' for solder connections. Starting at one end, measure off and mark the points that occur at each third of the element length. If the chart calls for an element length of 36', each point occurs at 12'; if the element length is to be 120', each point will occur at 40', etc. When the correct points have been marked, slip the end of the element through the eyes of two support insulators and slide each to a measured mark. Secure the insulators at this position on the antenna element by crimping the wire and wrapping it to the insulator with hook-up wire or by tying it firmly with stiff twine. Tape the element to the insulator for added protection against slippage. Proceed to the two ends of the antenna element and strip off the insulation for a length of 6".

Bring the two ends together and twist them for a temporary connection. If you will be using the delta loop for transmitting, you should install a 4:1 balun at the feedpoint of the antenna (available from the Radio Works Inc., P.O. Box 6159, Portsmouth, VA 23703 for $22.95). Now slip the support ropes through the eyes of the two support insulators. Secure them by tying tightly and pulling them to the mounting position—adjust the slack so that a nearly horizontal attitude is assumed by the top portion. Be certain that the supports are high enough to allow the dangling side sections to clear the earth completely after the top section of the delta loop appears to be secure. Separate the twisted ends of the antenna element and slide them through the opposite eyes of one ceramic insulator. Twist the bare copper wire back on itself at each side, and cut away any excess wire, but do not solder these connections yet.

Prepare the coaxial cable by stripping off the insulation for about 6". Separate the inner and the outer conductors, twist one to each side of the insulator connections, and wind them with the bare copper wires of the antenna ends (if you are using a balun, simply attach a PL-259 connector to each end of the cable). You can now solder at several points on each side. Next, tie a small length of clothesline rope to the center of the bottom insulator. You can now completely tape the entire bottom assembly; make certain that the entire insulator is covered as well as the coaxial transmission line. Now drive a small wooden stake into the earth near the point where the bottom tip of the delta loop will be attached. Tie the clothesline rope to this stake and take up any slack that prevents the element section from being held straight and firm.

The coaxial cable can be buried beneath the soil along its path back to the receiver or it can be connected to the side of a house. It can even be left lying in the yard, but because of the hazards for mowing and tripping, this practice is definitely not recommended.

Connect the coaxial cable to the shortwave receiver. You should notice excellent reception immediately after you adjust the antenna trimmer (if your receiver has this control) for loudest receiver output. Inspect the delta loop regularly to make sure that the antenna does not begin to droop as a result of possible stretching of the copper wire and support ropes. Frequent adjustments will probably be necessary for the first few months of use. After this period, the antenna element materials will stabilize and should not change their dimensions.

Conclusion

The antenna projects covered in this chapter are ideal for the beginner or intermediate antenna builder. For that matter, complexity does not necessarily make a fantastic antenna. Many of the antennas in this chapter will provide excellent shortwave radio reception.

Almost any antenna will provide many years of service if you construct it carefully and follow correct weatherproofing procedures. These basic projects can be altered slightly, added to, and improved as your construction skills increase. Any of the antenna systems in this chapter will show a tremendous increase in signal reception over a simple whip antenna, which is often supplied with many of the portable shortwave receivers on the modern market.

8
CHAPTER

Indoor and limited-space antennas

Except for the antenna projects in chapter 1, the construction projects and antenna theory covered so far have been for those antennas designed to be mounted outside. The physical space required by these antennas prohibit any other type of installation for the average shortwave listener. Many people are not fortunate enough to be situated in the center of vast amounts of flat and open acreage. However, the basic information covered thus far is useful to shortwave listeners who have limited antenna-mounting space available.

In the past, some potential shortwave listeners were deprived of this interesting hobby because of the apparent impossibility of installing conventional antenna systems. People who live in apartment complexes usually find that even if outside space is available, local restrictions prohibit outdoor antenna systems. However, many thousands of shortwave listeners hear excellent signals on their receivers with antenna systems mounted within the framework of the buildings in which they live.

Although the antennas in this chapter are effective and are electrically similar to full-length antennas, most do not perform quite as well as other full-sized antennas. Some people believe that because a radio "sees" a reduced-size antenna as being the same as a full-sized antenna, it will perform just as well. I disagree, but then, my opinion doesn't matter. If you like to experiment with antennas, you can build some designs from this chapter and compare them yourself. If you don't have the real estate to build a full-sized antenna, you are forced to use limited-spaced antennas anyway. In this case, these antennas are hobby savers.

Indoor antennas

An indoor antenna for shortwave might seem to be a farfetched idea until you consider that almost every AM radio—from the transistor pocket portable to the largest console model—is equipped with an internal antenna. This little ferrite loop is used exclusively for reception of AM signals. This type of antenna is not only indoors but is further encased within the radio cabinet in close proximity to circuitry, wiring, and the aluminum chassis. The same general idea applies to the indoor shortwave antenna, but you can make a considerable improvement by mounting its shortwave counterpart away from any metal object or signal obstructions. True, an outdoor antenna would (in most instances) provide better reception, but you can still obtain excellent results from a carefully constructed indoor system.

Indoor antennas have been built from aluminum foil, coat hangers, aluminum tubing, random wires, and even burglar alarm tape. If your desire to be a shortwave listener is great enough, you will find a way to construct the best antenna system possible within the restrictions imposed.

The first step in building an efficient indoor antenna is to obtain information about the construction materials used in the building where the system is to be mounted. Architectural plans and drawings are probably available, but if they cannot be found, an examination by a qualified building contractor or other knowledgeable individual should provide the answers. Or try a stud finder, which detects metal nails, to locate wires and conduit. Stud finders are available at Radio Shack. Look for the presence of steel support rods or any other large metal objects (no, Ozzy Osbourne posters won't hurt reception) that might present a null or deadspot in reception. If your shortwave antenna is close to any of these materials, they will cause a substantial amount of detuning to the system and hinder proper operation. Wood, brick, and cinderblock materials have a much smaller effect on the antenna because they do not normally conduct electrical signals.

If possible, it can't hurt to dig up drawings of the electrical wiring system for your building. Shortwave antennas should be kept away from large concentrations of this wiring—especially where hidden conduit and junction boxes are located. Carefully study the building plans to reveal a clear area where the mounting of an indoor antenna will be most advantageous. Of course, these plans might not be available to you. If that's the case, all you can do is experiment and hope that you find the best location as soon as possible.

When installing an antenna, always choose a location that is away from where people must walk. Little is more annoying than getting caught in other people's wire; likewise, it is equally annoying to have your antenna constantly being ripped down. The attic of a home or building is usually an ideal mounting area for most indoor antenna systems. These areas are usually relatively free from disturbance and have the added advantage of less steel and wiring than other portions of the building. An attic-mounted antenna has one further advantage—it is located at the highest mounting point available, which usually improves the reception of radio signals (Fig. 8-1). Apartment dwellers who have the advantage of being located on the top floor in a modern building might discover that the attic (if there is one) is quite long and can accommodate a full-size dipole or straight wire antenna. The antenna transmission line can then be dropped through the ceiling to the receiver operating position. Different types of buildings might present unusual antenna-mounting problems, but they might also offer some unusual advantages if you carefully study the situation.

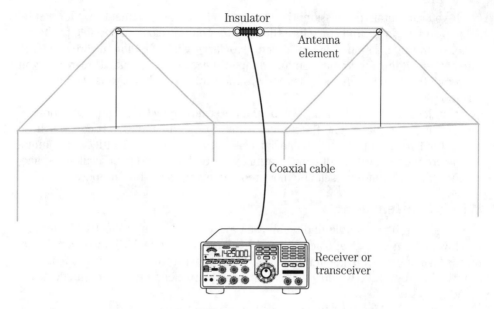

8-1 A shortened attic dipole.

Grounding

It is usually a good idea to locate an indoor antenna system on the top floor of a tall apartment building, but this added advantage applies only when balanced antennas (such as dipoles and inverted-Vs) are used. When an antenna such as a vertical is required, the top-floor advantage quickly vanishes because of the difficulty in obtaining a proper ground for the base of such an antenna. However, as stated elsewhere, MFJ Enterprises now offers an artificial ground. This little box allows you to have a ground—and to tune it as well. An artificial ground is great for apartment dwellers.

These days, many of the shortwave receivers on the market are portables that have built-in whip antennas. If you want to connect an auxiliary antenna to one of these portables, no ground system is required for the receiver to operate well. An outside antenna for a portable radio should have a ground connection, but that is more for safety reasons than for receiver performance.

Obtaining a good ground in most modern apartment complexes is often very difficult, regardless of the floor on which you reside. Many modern structures have resorted to plastic water pipe systems that provide no ground at all. Again, architectural plans of the building will be valuable in determining the type of system your building has. When metal water pipe is available, a ground connection to the cold-water pipe might be sufficient in many instances. The lack of a proper buried grounding network can be overcome by installing a few copper wires at the base of a vertical antenna, as is done in the ground-plane configuration (described in chapter 7). However, this type of ground can be inconvenient because of the necessity of running these wires on the floor, which causes a safety hazard to persons walking through.

If you can obtain permission, the best ground for the apartment dweller can be made by driving a ground stake into the soil at a point as close as possible to the receiver operating position. Then, run a length of large-gauge aluminum wire down the side of the building for connection to the top of the grounding stake. However, if you are a radio amateur, such a long lead to ground probably will not work well because it is too inefficient.

Your location in the building will be the determining factor for antenna choices. Persons living on the ground floor might want to erect an indoor vertical, but those on the top floor might opt for a balanced system to avoid the difficulties of obtaining a good ground. Regardless of your location, your building, and your available space, an efficient indoor antenna can be mounted and made to operate properly.

Window antennas

When you have trouble finding an area away from metal or electrical wiring, a window is the next logical place to consider. Try to find one with a wooden frame, rather than one with an aluminum frame (common with storm windows). Most locations on or around the window will provide adequate clearance to mount some sort of indoor system.

If you are looking for window glass-mounted antennas, see the window screen and suction cup design (Fig. 8-2) in chapter 1. I like this design a lot because it is functional, very portable, and it doesn't restrict the use of the window. Another possibility when space is at an absolute minimum is the burglar alarm tape antenna (Fig. 8-3). This tape is available at most electronic supply stores and it can be easily removed at any time. Burglar alarm tape is thin aluminum foil with an adhesive backing. It is used as part of an alarm system should the window be broken.

Another type of antenna that attaches to the windowsill is a vertical design that runs the length of the window and is attached to a loading coil made up of several turns of copper wire. The size of the loading coil depends on the frequency or frequencies to be received. Loaded antennas of this type are popular for limited-space, indoor, and mobile uses.

Indoor hidden antennas

Sometimes it becomes necessary to install an antenna within a room while hiding the fact that it's there at all. This preserves the room's original condition without showing any signs of wires or cables. Many rooms have been paneled and include molding strips along the line where the ceiling and panel sections meet. In rooms that have these ceiling molding strips, you can remove the strips, mount the antenna wires, and then tack the strips into their original positions. Of course, if you remove (and subsequently damage) the strips without the permission of your landlord, you could cause some serious tensions. Whatever you choose to do, make a wise decision!

The receiver transmission line should be attached at a point in the antenna element that is closest to the receiver, preferably in a corner, and painted to hide its presence. It is usually best to connect some type of tuning device between the receiver and the transmission line when using antennas of this type to allow efficient coverage of several different shortwave frequencies. When properly installed, an antenna of this design should last for the duration of residence at that location. It can be removed in minutes by detaching the molding strips and simply pulling down the element wiring.

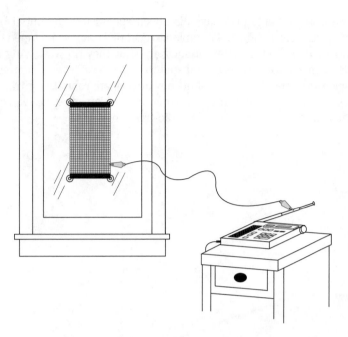

8-2 The window screen antenna.

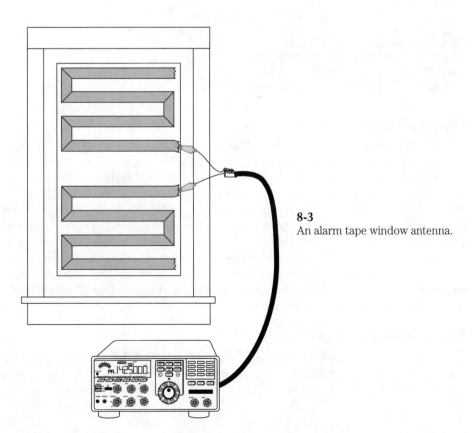

8-3
An alarm tape window antenna.

Shortwave-listening antennas have also been successfully mounted behind wall paneling, along baseboards (Fig. 8-4), stapled to coat racks, and even taped under rugs. These are highly unorthodox mounting methods, but they do work. Any reasonably clear area can be made to serve as a good spot to place the shortwave antenna. Antennas of this sort work fine for listening, but they are not appropriate for transmitting. If you run a high-powered transmitter into one of these hidden antennas, you could cause a fire or burn someone with the powerful radio-frequency fields.

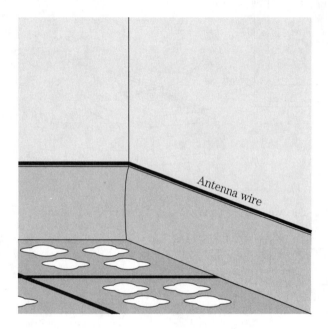

8-4
An antenna mounted at the baseboard.

Unintentional antennas

An *unintentional antenna* is a structure or portion of a structure that was originally designed to serve other purposes. A good example of an unintentional antenna would be the springs of a bed, which have been used at times with some success. A few other possibilities include metal roofs, metal railings, and aluminum-edged storm windows. Though not an indoor antenna system, common roof guttering, which is used to channel water from the side of a roof to culverts on the ground, has been used successfully as a shortwave antenna system. The main consideration in antennas of this unusual nature is a considerable length of ungrounded metal or wire that can be conveniently connected to the receiver by a simple transmission line. With a little imagination, a large variety of unconventional objects could serve as fair shortwave antenna systems.

More indoor antenna ideas

Some good indoor antenna systems can be fabricated from existing antenna structures. Standard television antennas can be made to perform fairly well on the shortwave frequencies when not in use for their designed purposes. A television antenna that is fed with twin-lead cable will receive shortwave signals well when the bare ends of the cable, which normally attach to the television set terminals, are twisted together and connected to the antenna terminal of the shortwave receiver. This effectively changes the television transmission line into a solid antenna element, which is supported many feet in the air by the television antenna. The same principle applies to FM, scanner, and other types of twin-lead connected antennas. Some antennas of this variety are fed with coaxial cable. These systems are best connected to the shortwave receiver by means of an alligator clip lead. One end of the lead is connected to the outside conductor or braid of the coaxial cable.

Cables that are supplied with standard metal-cased connectors usually have the braid attached to the metal shell, and it is a simple job to clip onto the edge of this case. The same principle applies as with the twin-lead cable. The element consists of a stranded braid conductor, which runs for a considerable length to a termination located at the original antenna.

Some larger apartment complexes provide laundry rooms for tenants and, in some instances, indoor metal-stranded clotheslines that are of considerable length. If permission can be obtained from the landlord, it might be possible to connect these lines with a section of coaxial cable or twin-lead. Unfortunately, most laundry rooms are located in the basements of buildings, which are not ideal antenna mounting areas, but if this is the only means of listening to signals, use it. Clotheslines (in general) make excellent antennas if made from wire, so even an outside version might be utilized to provide a receiver connection (Fig. 8-5). Coaxial cable could be buried under the soil to the support pole and then run up its side for a connection to the horizontal line. It might be necessary to insulate both ends of this line.

There are problems with any antenna design. There are also advantages. The main idea with a limited-space antenna design is to work around the problems in order to enjoy the advantages.

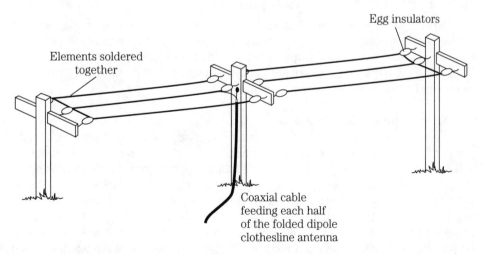

8-5 A clothesline antenna.

By now, it should be apparent that almost anything made of metal can be used as a shortwave antenna system. While reading this chapter, look around and find several objects or utilities that you have never considered before as shortwave antenna possibilities. Just because an object doesn't look anything like a standard antenna doesn't mean that it won't work. It probably will work . . . and surprisingly well, if you follow basic antenna principles. There is only one requirement any object has to meet to be a potential candidate for a shortwave transmitting antenna element—it must be able to conduct the energy generated by shortwave transmitters. For most intents and purposes, this means the object must be metallic. Taking this rule literally means that a frying pan, a tin roof, a curtain rod, and an endless list of other metallic objects could be used to receive radio signals on the shortwave frequencies. Some will work better than others, but all of them can be considered as shortwave antenna elements if you properly connect them to a receiver.

Points to remember

- Choose the highest location available.
- Choose an area that is relatively free of other metal obstructions.
- Plan the antenna mounting to require the smallest length of transmission line (twin-lead or coaxial cable) to the receiver.
- Make certain that the antenna, transmission line, and all associated hardware are out of heavily traveled areas to prevent accidents.
- Double-check all solder joints and connections.
- Make sure that the antenna does not cross any type of power cable or connection.
- Use your imagination and practical antenna theory.

If you follow these points, you will most likely have an efficient and safe indoor antenna system. Though highly unorthodox, the antenna systems mentioned will work, and many will work well when designed with care and planning.

Indoor antenna construction project

Between this chapter and chapter 1, you should have some basic understanding of the requirements for indoor antennas. The following construction projects are meant to be used as a guide to provide ideas for possible indoor antenna systems. Some modifications might be required, depending on the mounting location and other conditions peculiar to certain installations.

Alarm tape window antenna

If you weren't satisfied with the window screen antenna in chapter 1, you might want to try the alarm tape window antenna (Fig. 8-3). This project is easy to install and does not require any precise measurements. Apply as much tape as possible to the window while maintaining an inch or so of spacing between loops. If the window must be opened from time to time, run the tape along the window frame when crossing from a top section to the bottom. The tape can be cut at this point to allow the window to be opened and secured with alligator clips when it is closed. Possibly a better method would be to cut a piece of Plexiglas to the size of the window, place the tape on the Plexiglas (as you would for the previous example). Then, you could pull out the alarm tape antenna whenever you wanted to listen to shortwave, and you would still have full use of the window.

The parts list for the alarm tape antenna is very small, and each item should be available in most hobby or electronics stores (one of the best sources is your local Radio Shack). Look for the section that displays building supplies for home burglar alarm systems. The self-adhesive terminals are available in many different styles and designs. Any type should meet the requirements of this antenna design.

Differences in window designs require different tape installations patterns, but the main idea in building the antenna is to apply as much tape as possible. Measure and cut the tape for the length required to complete a vertical or horizontal strip on the window. Apply this strip carefully, removing all air bubbles from beneath the tape by rubbing it gently with your finger. A clean application surface will also make the entire installation easier. When the first strip is installed, cut another for the same length and apply it in the same manner. After you have taped down these long strips, cut small 1" or 2" sections to connect the tape into one continuous antenna element, by overlapping the large portions of tape with the smaller.

After you have installed the tape sections, look over every inch of the finished element to make certain no small breaks have occurred. Any breaks can be repaired simply by overlapping the gap with a short piece of tape. You can now install the small terminal strips at a convenient point on the window or window frame. Then, bring the ends of the antenna element out to the terminal strips from the connection.

When the entire antenna seems complete, brush the strips lightly with a clear lacquer (if possible). Lacquer will help to keep the antenna firm and secure; of course, your landlord probably will not appreciate having alarm tape lacquered all over one of the windows. Run the receiver transmission line to the terminal strips, one conductor to each strip, and to the shortwave receiver. RG-58U coaxial cable can also be used for the antenna transmission line, if you wish.

When you have made all connections to the receiver, tune in a weak signal and peak the antenna trimmer adjustment (if your receiver has one) for maximum strength. You might find that it is necessary to install a small variable capacitor across the antenna terminals for more adequate tuning control—especially if you used coaxial cable. These capacitors can also be found at your local Radio Shack. Look for a broadcast-band variable capacitor, which has a value of about 365 pF. Using a short length of wire, connect one contact of the capacitor to one of the antenna terminals at the window; attach the remaining contact on the capacitor to the other antenna terminal. Use trial-and-error tuning of the window capacitor and the antenna trimmer adjustment to determine the best settings for each shortwave frequency.

If the antenna fails to receive properly for any reason, the problem can probably be traced to a small break in the alarm tape element. You can easily check this by removing the receiver transmission line and placing the leads of an ohmmeter across the two terminal strips on the window. A very low reading of several ohms at the most should be obtained. A very high reading, or no reading at all, indicates a break, which you must locate by closely examining and repairing the tape (reapply alarm tape to that spot). A check of this sort is best made before the clear lacquer is applied, because a repair is much easier to make before the tape is covered.

Other problems that could hinder proper reception include a shorted or open conductor in the receiver transmission line. This can be checked with an ohmmeter connected to the conductors of the line. A low, or zero, resistance reading across the two conductors at the receiver end of the line when the line is not connected to the antenna element indicates a short. A very high, or infinite, reading across the same conductors with the line connected to the antenna element shows a break. The easiest correction for a defective receiver transmission line is to replace the faulty section or the entire line.

Limited-space antennas

Between the rural shortwave listener with plenty of antenna installation space and the cramped apartment dweller with hardly any space for an outdoor antenna lies another category that includes the majority of people who make radio listening a hobby. This group has adequate room to install some sort of antenna system until the length of antenna elements passes 60' or so, and then space problems arise. Almost everyone with a backyard in a small- to medium-sized community begins to consider space-saving antennas when lengths approach or exceed 60' to 100', which is the antenna space available on an average town or suburban house lot.

Antennas for limited space resemble the basic full-length antenna designs more so than the indoor systems because a smaller amount of element shrinking is required. For example, the basic dipole antenna can be extended for as far as space permits in a horizontal position, and then dropped vertically at each end to a point near the ground. The same amount of wire is used, but the configuration, or position the antenna assumes, is altered to fit into the available space. The inverted-V (covered in chapter 7) is a form of limited-space antenna; it consists of a dipole with the ends dropped diagonally to points near the ground.

Vertical antennas can be mounted with the element in a diagonal position in relation to the earth, if adequate room is not available to provide a wide enough radius for guy-wire supports. A vertical antenna for a frequency of approximately 4 MHz would require an antenna element of about 58' in height. If mounted diagonally, the same antenna can be attached to a 20' or 30' high support. The lower "ground" end of the element would then extend downward and outward for the distance required to reach the ground. This would be a sort of quarter-wavelength sloping "vertical."

An alternative method is to make the vertical antenna physically shorter while still maintaining the electrical length of 58'. This can be accomplished by inserting a loading coil somewhere along the vertical element. If the total physical height of the vertical element was only 15' or 20', self-supporting aluminum tubing could be used. Although you might be able to get by without using guy wires, it's always better to use guy wires on vertical structures. Another method of physically shortening the vertical element is to mount it in a horizontal position for a portion of its length and then drop it vertically to its ground connection point. This method does not require the use of loading coils, which are sometimes mechanically difficult to install. Also, using loading coils means that the vertical element must be assembled from several pieces with a loading coil in between. When loading coils are used in this manner, it is difficult to properly strengthen the antenna.

The hybrid tubing/wire vertical

The side of a building serves as a good support when it is otherwise impossible to mount a vertical antenna in an open area. So, in some situations, you might consider a hybrid tubing/wire antenna (Fig. 8-6) to achieve a sort of random-length vertical longwire. A short length of aluminum tubing can be installed on the roof for a height of 10' or 15'. Drill a small hole at the base of the tubing and make sure that you have enough wire to run from the base of the tubing to several feet above the ground. Solder a noninsulated ring terminal (available in many different sizes from Mouser Electronics, 12 Emery Ave., Randolph, NJ 07869, and elsewhere) to the end of the wire and bolt it into the tubing. Then, run the wire down the side of the building with insulated standoffs and stake it off so that the antenna wire ends at a point just above the ground. The top of the antenna element (the aluminum tubing) extends to a considerable height above the roof and the remainder of the antenna is composed of the length of wire mounted to the side of the building.

Much of a vertical antenna's efficiency is determined by the height of the top end above ground and its distance from surrounding objects. With this in mind, it is best to make any alterations in the vertical plane of the element at a point nearer the ground. In other words, if a portion of the element must be run horizontally, it is best to do this near the ground end. When loading coils are installed, the opposite is true. A coil at the far end or near the top is more advantageous.

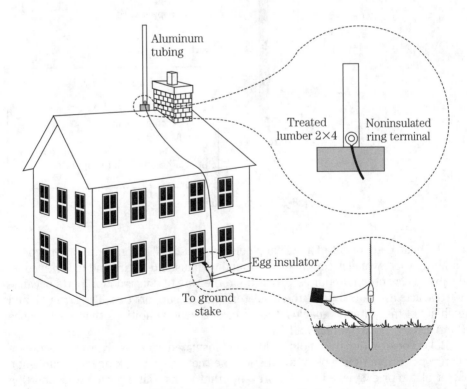

8-6 A hybrid wire/tubing vertical.

The helical dipole antenna

You can substantially reduce the physical length of an antenna element by using a loading coil as its entire length. The *helically wound antenna* (Fig. 8-7) uses an insulated, rigid support, which is wound from bottom to top with insulated copper wire. Helically wound antennas are more evenly balanced than those that use a large coil at only one point in the element. The helix winding method can be used with almost any type of antenna, including horizontal dipoles. Although a vertical antenna uses a firm coil support, such as a fiberglass or bamboo pole, the helically wound dipole uses nylon rope to support the coils and at the same time remains reasonably flexible. Better yet, the helically wound dipole is not a compensation antenna—it is a full-length design that performs quite well. In fact, some hobbyists insist that the helically wound dipole performs even better than the standard dipole. One advantage of the helically wound dipole is that because of the extra wire area used, the antenna is usable over a broader frequency range than the standard dipole (i.e., it has a lower Q).

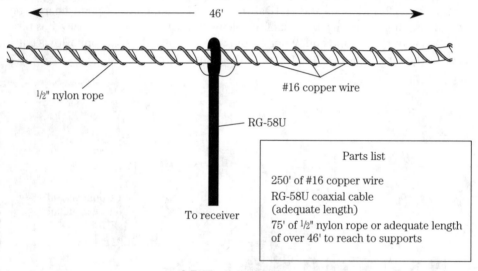

46'

½" nylon rope

#16 copper wire

RG-58U

To receiver

Parts list

250' of #16 copper wire
RG-58U coaxial cable
(adequate length)
75' of ½" nylon rope or adequate length
of over 46' to reach to supports

8-7 The helical dipole.

The main component of a helical dipole antenna is ½" nylon (or another type of synthetic) rope, which is continuously wound with insulated wire and fed with coaxial cable. This antenna requires very little in the way of construction parts because the rope acts as the coil form, the insulator, and the support ties. The strength and flexibility of this antenna enables it to withstand wind conditions that would cause other wire antennas to break and fall.

Begin construction by winding 200 feet of insulated wire evenly over a section of nylon rope (or another type of synthetic rope that won't break down in sunlight). Use insulated or enamelled wire to prevent other turns, water, or ice from shorting out the antenna and rendering it ineffective. Leave plenty of extra rope so that the antenna can be tied to the two antenna supports. Having one solid length of antenna with no connections or insulators is a handy advantage, and it makes the actual construction of the helically wound dipole quite easy.

The difficult aspect of constructing the helically wound dipole is winding that much wire on a rope. Perhaps the easiest method to wind the wire onto the rope is to attach the one end of the wire to the rope with several turns of duct tape. From that point, wrap the wire in the grooves of the rope to help hold it in place and it will make it easy for you to keep the windings tight and evenly spaced. Keep winding the antenna until you have wound all of the wire on the rope. When the winding is complete, secure each end of the long coil by tightly tying the ends with insulated wire.

Next, find the center point of the antenna element. Measure from one end to find the total element length, divide the total length by 2, and cut the wire at this point. To make the connections to the coaxial cable transmission line, scrape or peel the insulation from about 2" from each wire lead at the antenna center. Bare the copper wire to enable a good solder connection to the transmission line. Strip the coaxial cable for 5" and separate the center conductor and the outer braid. Loop the cable around the center of the antenna, as you would for the standard dipole. Then, tightly wrap wire around the cable at the rope to anchor it in place.

Now, twist and solder the ends of the coaxial cable directly to the two coil leads. Tape all solder joints for protection. For a longer service life, the entire coil section of the antenna can be covered with tape or, possibly, a weatherproofing paint. Tape or paint will also help keep the coiled wire in place and prevent it from slipping. Installing the helically wound dipole is relatively easy; just follow the directions for installing the inverted-V antenna in chapter 7.

This antenna is very simple and inexpensive to build. No ceramic insulators are needed because the rope acts as one long strand of insulating material. The enamel-coated wire is available at most hobby stores and is identified by a shiny black or copper color. The helical dipole also has the added advantage of being very portable. It can be removed from a mounting position in minutes, coiled in the trunk of a car, and installed quickly at a new location.

Practically nothing can go wrong with this antenna, short of a defective transmission line, which can be checked in the same manner as for dipole antennas. A break in the helical coil is more serious and is often difficult to repair.

This helical winding design can be used to build a vertical antenna that is only half the length of the dipole. Simply build one side of the dipole and mount it vertically with a buried ground system. Only half of the components to build the dipole would be required. The rope ends of the antenna could be tied to an overhead support and to a ground stake at the antenna base. Only half as much enamel wire is required, and probably less coaxial cable is required as well. Tuning and check-out procedures for this helical wound vertical would be the same as for all vertical antennas that are fed by coaxial cable.

The total length of the wound copper wire is about twice the length required for a full-sized antenna of the same design, but the continuous winding allows each element to be as short as 5' or 6'. The total length of the support insulator can vary, but the longer types provide better performance.

The coil-loaded vertical antenna

The version of the coil-loaded vertical antenna in this section (Fig. 8-8) performs well over most of the shortwave frequencies, and it requires a total height of only 15.5'; the full-length version would extend to almost 40'. This antenna should be erected as far as possible from any surrounding objects and supplied with a good earth ground system (see chapter 6 on ground systems). Each ground wire should be at least 16' long. The added length increases the efficiency of this antenna.

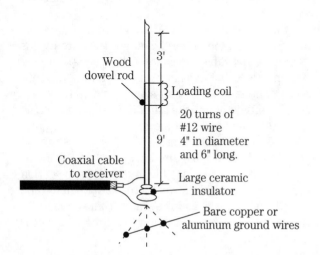

Parts list

1 3' section of 3/4" aluminum tubing
1 9' section of 3/4" aluminum tubing
3 aluminum or copper bare wires
1 large ceramic insulator
1 10" length of 5/8" dowel rod
1 4" diameter coil form
Adequate amount of RG-58U
Coaxial cable to reach receiver
3 1" metal cutting screws
60' of nylon clothesline rope
30' #12 solid wire

8-8 A coil-loaded vertical.

The main element is constructed of two sections of lightweight aluminum tubing available at many hardware stores. Cut one section to 3' long and cut the other to 9' long. Insert a 10" section of a wooden dowel rod in the end of the longer tubing section for about 2". The smaller piece of tubing fits over the other end of the dowel rod. A tight fit is needed at this point. If the dowel is loose in the tubing, choose a slightly larger diameter of wooden rod. Using a hand drill, make two holes in the aluminum sections about a ½" from the ends that the dowel rod is fitted through.

After you have drilled the holes, insert a self-tapping screw in each and tighten just enough to allow a small portion of the shafts to protrude from the tubing surface. Drill a similar hole in the far end of the longest tubing section about 1" from the end. Insert the remaining screw and tighten as before. This portion of construction is complete.

Next, wind 20 turns of #12 solid copper wire onto a 4" diameter coil form. This form can be made from any insulated material, such as varnished wood, ceramic, or plexiglass. Refer to chapter 2 for explicit directions for winding coils. The turns can be closely wound at first and then spaced evenly to fill up the entire form. Allow several inches of wire to remain at each end of the coil to connect to the aluminum element sections. After you wind and space the coil, coat it with a clear varnish or other protective material. Allow it to dry for several hours.

Install the coil on the antenna element by wrapping the ends of the copper wires around the protruding screws on each side of the dowel rod. Use a high-wattage soldering iron or soldering gun and solder each wire to the screws. Check each of the two connections for good solder joints. Clip off any remaining fragments of copper wire that might protrude from the connections.

Now, install the ground wires outward from the intended base of the antenna, like the spokes of a wheel. Allow about 1' of wire from each wire to protrude from the ground at the antenna base. After the wires are buried, twist the protruding ends together and solder at several points. Now, place the bottom insulator in position to mount the antenna.

This type of antenna, though short, needs to be supported by three guy ropes. Tie standard nylon clothesline rope below the loading coil and extend it to three points on the ground. Place the bottom end of the longer element over the ceramic insulator and press it in for a solid fit. If you can't find a functional ceramic insulator, try slipping the end of the tubing over the top of a narrow-mouthed bottle (such as an older-style 16-ounce glass pop bottle). Hoist the antenna element to its vertical position carefully. Don't suddenly pull or jerk the element, which might loosen the antenna loading coil and dowel rod connection. When the element is vertical, tie off the guy ropes and examine the structure for any weaknesses or tendencies to sway.

You can now run the coaxial cable to the base of the vertical antenna. Solder a PL-259 connector on the end of the coaxial cable (if your receiver has one of these connections), following the methods described in chapter 3. Prepare the other end of the coaxial cable as you would for a standard dipole and solder a noninsulated ring terminal to the end of the center conductor and screw it into the tubing. Firmly solder the center conductor of the cable to the base screw of the aluminum tubing. Then, twist the braid and the copper ground wires together for several inches and solder this joint. Tape the solder connections to avoid weather deterioration. The antenna is complete.

Connect the coaxial cable to the shortwave receiver antenna post and tune the trimmer for strongest reception. This antenna should work well for all but the lowest shortwave frequencies.

The coil-loaded longwire

The *coil-loaded longwire antenna* (Fig. 8-9) offers many conveniences for the shortwave listener. Almost any length of wire can be used for the antenna element and all bands can be tuned from the receiver operating position if you connect the antenna to an antenna tuner near the receiver. The receiver and antenna tuner would then be connected by a short section of coaxial cable.

I generally consider any wire that's over 100' to be a longwire antenna. Some others consider a true longwire antenna to be at least a full wavelength from end to end. I choose the "100' rule" because under the "full-wavelength rule," an antenna is a "longwire" for some frequencies and not others. This confusion seems totally unnecessary for general shortwave-listening applications.

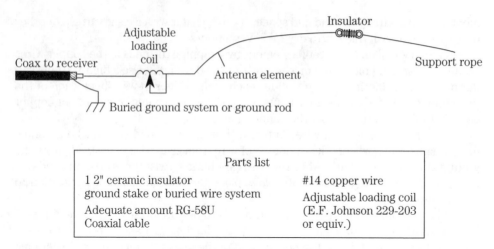

8-9 A coil-loaded longwire.

This shortened version of the longwire uses a variable inductor or adjustable coil to electrically lengthen the shorter wire that is used for the main element. Commercially manufactured loading coils can be expensive, but you can sometimes get excellent buys at hamfests, surplus outlet stores, and catalogs. The tuning coil can be mounted on a wood or an aluminum chassis or it can be connected directly to a wall or table.

Always use the longest antenna element that can be accommodated by the space available. Taking the small insulator, insert one end of the antenna element, secure it by twisting, and solder. Connect the other end of the insulator to the support rope, which you (in turn) tie off to a distant support. String the remaining end of the antenna element to the fixed position of the antenna tuning coil; clip or solder it to one of the two contacts. Make certain that the element is not too tight or too loose.

A good base on which to mount the coil and the connections for the longwire is a small board. You might even want to cut a decorative edge onto the board with a router. Some sanding and wood stain also improve the looks of the board. With the coil and terminals mounted on a finished board, the project will look much like some early radio equipment from the 1920s. Then, you can secure a small terminal at each end of the coil to mount it onto the wood.

Make the remaining connection from the center conductor of the coaxial cable to the remaining contact on the tuning coil. Bare the center conductor for an inch or two and wrap it around the terminal. Depending on the type of terminal you used, either clip the center conductor in place or solder it. Connect the remaining conductor (the braid of the coaxial cable) to the ground system, which can be made of several wires just beneath the soil or a 4' to 6' copper (or copper-clad) ground stake (or pipe) driven into the earth. The limited-space longwire is not as dependent on a ground system as the quarter-wavelength vertical. However, performance is always best with a good ground system.

Solder or connect the longwire antenna to the other (input) terminal of the tuning coil. Then, cut a 1' piece of insulated hookup wire and remove 2" of insulation at either end. Solder one end of the wire to the input terminal of the loading coil (the side where the antenna is held in place) and solder an alligator clip on the other end of the wire.

Fit the receiver end of the coaxial cable with a connector to match the receiver input terminal (probably a PL-259, if you have a "table top" receiver), and the coil-loaded longwire antenna is ready for use. This is one of the simplest antenna projects covered (except for the projects in chapter 1), and its performance ranges from good to excellent in most mounting configurations.

To tune the antenna, adjust the receiver antenna trim control (if your receiver has one) for maximum signal strength. Another antenna tuning adjustment is to change the tap on the loading coil. To do this, attach the alligator clip from the antenna element to different loops on the tuning coil. Less coil should work better at higher frequencies, and more coil will generally be required at lower frequencies. Each change of the coil will probably affect the setting of the trim control. You need to do some trial-and-error to determine the best combinations of settings for each frequency to be covered. When you have found the best settings, write them down for future use.

Problems that develop with the longwire antenna are very easily checked because you can complete all testing at or near the operating position. The only points that could cause faulty operation are the solder connections at the tuning coil and shorted or open conductors in the receiver transmission line.

The trap dipole

The *trap dipole* (Fig. 8-10) is actually a full-sized antenna, but traps are used at certain lengths in the antenna element to provide multifrequency coverage of the shortwave bands. A *trap* differs from a loading coil in that it is a complete circuit unto itself. A loading coil works with the antenna element to electrically lengthen it, but a trap serves to provide a high resistance at specific frequencies to effectively isolate portions of the element. Other frequencies are allowed to pass through the trap to utilize the full length of the antenna. The trap dipole uses only the first element (before the first trap) on either side of the center insulator for reception on the higher frequencies. Lower frequencies are received on larger sections of the antenna system. Thus, the antenna can be tuned, or switched, for optimum coverage on many frequencies automatically.

Uses for this antenna in a limited-space situation include covering many shortwave frequencies without installing several different dipoles. As mentioned before, this antenna is practically a full-sized design, but only one element is used for multifrequency coverage. Alternative antennas to the trap dipole are the multiband cage dipole and the multiband vertical.

Begin this project by measuring out copper wire for the lowest frequency band that you plan to use with the antenna. Allow about 1' additional for error and to the connect to the ceramic insulators. Then, construct a standard dipole (follow the directions in chapter 7). Next, find the length of the highest frequency band that you plan to use with the antenna. Divide that number by 2 and measure that distance away from the center on each side of the antenna. Add an extra inch onto each side and cut the antenna elements at these two locations.

The next step is to cut and install the coil forms for the antenna traps. A length of 2.5" diameter PVC pipe is excellent for this application. After you cut the PVC pipe to 2" long pieces, drill a small hole at the ends of each piece. Run about 1" of the antenna element through the hole at one end of the 2" PVC pipe sec-

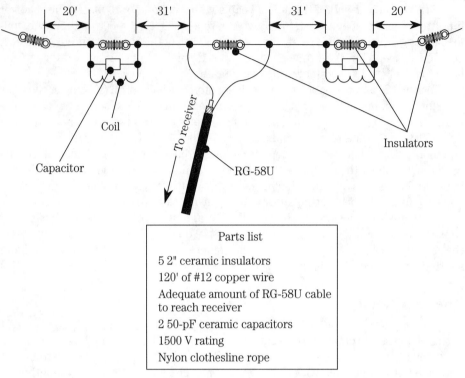

8-10 A trap-loaded dipole.

tion. Run about 1" of the antenna element that you cut off through the hole at the other end of the 2" PVC pipe section. Twist that piece of wire back upon itself. Follow the same process for the other side of the antenna.

Next, build the traps on the PVC coil forms. Each trap is a coil consisting of 16 turns of #14 bare copper wire evenly spaced on the 2.5" diameter PVC for a length of 2". Wind these coils securely and then twist the first turn of the coil in with the twists of the antenna elements. Now, pull out a 50-pF disc capacitor and twist its leads in with the twisted antenna elements and coil ends. Solder each connection joint carefully. Now, coat the entire trap assembly with a large amount of fiberglass resin (follow the directions on the can) for stability and weatherproofing. Wrap all solder connections with weatherproof tape.

If you want to add traps for other bands, divide the distance by two, measure that distance out from the center (where the coaxial cable feeds the antenna) on each side. Then, add an extra 1" on each side for soldering losses. Follow the instructions in the previous two paragraphs to construct and install traps in this part of the antenna. It is very common for trap dipoles to contain elements for three or four different antennas, so enjoy custom-designing your own trap dipole.

The trap dipole can now be hoisted into position. The installation instructions for this antenna are the same as the multiband cage dipole in chapter 7. Like the multiband cage dipole, this antenna is best installed in a clear area. Otherwise, it is sure to get stuck in trees. Then, connect the end of the coaxial cable to the short-wave receiver and listen to the strength of the signals on the radio. Tune the antenna trim control (if your radio has one) for the strongest signals. You must peak this control each time that you switch bands on the receiver.

You can check the trap dipole using the same techniques as for the basic dipole antenna (see chapter 7). With all of the traps (and connections in each trap), you could easily have an open circuit. It is very important to solder each joint properly and to check your work carefully. If the antenna doesn't operate properly, you will have to pull it back down and check the joints until you locate the problem.

The trap vertical antenna

The *trap vertical antenna* (Fig. 8-11) is designed to be mounted on a sturdy wooden mast or the top of a building. Its operation is similar to the trap dipole, covered in the previous section. The main body of the antenna element is made of three sections of aluminum conduit, which is available at most hardware stores and electrical supply outlets. The insulators should be at least 8" long and be sturdy enough to support the weight of the antenna element sections.

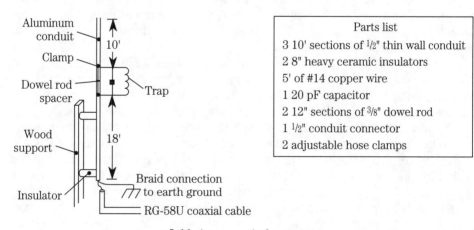

Parts list
3 10' sections of 1/2" thin wall conduit
2 8" heavy ceramic insulators
5' of #14 copper wire
1 20 pF capacitor
2 12" sections of 3/8" dowel rod
1 1/2" conduit connector
2 adjustable hose clamps

8-11 A trap vertical antenna.

First, cut 2' from one of the 10' conduit sections and connect the remaining 8' to another section with the conduit connector. Clean the two connecting ends of all corrosion and dirt, because a good electrical connection is important. The finished result should be 10' and 18' sections of conduit. Now, using a hacksaw, make two even cuts in one end of each section for about 3". These cuts allow the dowel rod to slip into the ends much easier. When you have made the cuts, slide an adjustable hose clamp over each end and tighten just enough to allow slide adjustments. Insert the dowel rod into each section for a length of 3" on each side. Now, guide the clamps to a point that is 0.5" from the section ends and tighten them completely for a strong mechanical joint. Test this connection to make certain that the two sections can't slip.

Wind the coil for the trap at this point in the same manner as described for the trap dipole. In this project, make the coil form 2" in diameter. Wind 11 turns of #14 copper wire onto the form and space the turns evenly for a length of 2". Now, solder the 20-pF capacitor to the coil with one capacitor lead connected to each end of the coil. Allow about 4" of extra wire at each end of the coil for antenna connections. Then, solder a noninsulated ring terminal (available in many different sizes from Mouser Electronics, 12 Emery Ave., Randolph, NJ 07869) to each end of the coil. When you have completed the coil and capacitor wiring, coat the trap with epoxy cement and allow it to dry for several hours.

Drill one small hole in each piece of conduit—approximately 2" from the edges at the center, where the dowel is. Slide the finished trap over the conduit and slightly loosen the two adjustable clamps. Insert the ends of the coil conductor through the clamps and retighten the connection. Then, with a screw, attach each ring terminal into a hole. Make certain that the joints at the coil and between the two element sections are solid.

Attach the two large ceramic insulators to the wooden mast or to the side of a building. Drill holes in the conduit at the two or three points where the antenna will be anchored. To install the trap vertical antenna, follow the directions for installing the quarter-wave vertical in chapter 7. Lift the entire element onto the mast and align the holes with the ceramic insulators. Fit the shafts through the element and tighten the nuts for a solid mounting.

Attach the connector (probably a PL-259 if you have a table-top receiver) to the one end of the coaxial cable and strip it. Connect the other end to the base of the vertical, according to the instructions in chapter 3 and in the quarter-wavelength vertical antenna section in chapter 7. The antenna is now ready for use.

No reception is almost always the result of a defective transmission line or a bad connection of the coaxial cable to the base of the antenna. Intermittent reception is usually the result of a bad connection at the trap near the center of the element. If you recheck all connections, you should be able to correct the situation. Good signal reception of only a few shortwave bands could point to a defective capacitor at the antenna trap. If this is the case, replace the capacitor. Make certain that all connections, especially the one between the top element and the wooden dowel rod, are secure. If the sections are loose at this point, it could cause the top section to eventually fall and possibly cause serious injury to anyone standing near the antenna system.

Other ideas for limited-space antennas

Chapter 7 featured some information on combining two different types of elements into one system. The same logic applies to limited-space antennas, particularly where the two designs are similar. For example, the helically wound rope dipole could be combined with a helically wound vertical to form a system that receives signals well, regardless of the polarization of the transmitting antenna. Almost every basic design can be altered to a shortened version, regardless of the element complexity or of the mounting pattern. This book is intended as a basis for antenna designs as well as a means to understand antenna principles more completely. Use the ideas you have with the knowledge you've gained to design an antenna that performs well within your particular limitations.

9
CHAPTER

Portable antenna systems

Often shortwave listeners yearn to be away from the noise of the cities and tall buildings that obstruct the path of many of the rarer signals. A high peak or hilltop looks awfully inviting on those days when all that seems to come over the bands is garbled voices and ear-shattering static. This dream of a lonely and isolated spot ideal for shortwave listening can become a reality because of the abundance of portable receivers and those that can be operated from a 12-V battery. Even ac-only receivers can be powered by an automobile battery if an inexpensive power inverter is used (however, the "buzz" interference from the inverter will probably be more bothersome than the interference that you would face at home).

So, the problem of supplying power to the receiver is not a large one at all, but when antenna considerations are brought into this rosy picture all but the very daring tend to give up on the entire idea. True, whip antennas could be used, but they are not particularly efficient and any advantage that might have been gained by a high and remote location would be quickly lost when all receiving must be done on a little metal rod that only poses as a shortwave antenna.

The thrill of ideal receiving conditions can be attained in a very easy and inexpensive way, by building your own portable antenna system for shortwave listening. This type of antenna must be able to be stowed away in the trunk of an automobile, unpacked easily, and mounted in a reasonably short period of time. Most full-sized wire antennas can be modified or converted in some way to meet these conditions. The end result is an ideal reception area on some lofty peak and an antenna that is just as efficient (or more efficient) as an antenna that occupies the backyard in the city.

Important portable antenna qualities

Portable antennas generally differ from permanent ones in weight, element stability, and means of support. When compactness is necessary for storage in small areas, even more differences might exist. Ruggedness is also an important factor because antennas that are continually moved and remounted must endure much more bending of elements and general abuse than a fixed system, which is usually left in place for most of its active life. Below is a list of requirements for most portable antenna designs.

- Flexible antenna wire
- Single wire or coaxial cable transmission line
- Compact and light enough to be carried by one person when collapsed
- Quickly assembled and mounted
- Easily collapsed and stored

Portable antennas that meet these five requirements can easily be constructed in a matter of a few hours.

Flexibility

To build an antenna resistant to inevitable rough treatment, you should go with a heavier gauge of stranded wire. However, the very light gauges of wire make your antennas smaller and easier to transport. My favorite types of antenna wire are #14 house wiring with heavy-duty insulation and #26 solid wire with teflon insulation. I like the #14 wire for the more complicated, permanent, balanced antennas, such as dipoles and single-element loops. The #26 solid wire is excellent for longwires, Vs, and simple, portable longwires.

Some people suggest using very light-gauge wire to build dipoles for mobile use. This is a bad choice because the wires are too weak to support the coaxial cable in the center. Also, the wires are very easy to tangle when attempting to hang the dipole. Unless you plan to use the dipole indoors with only about 3' or 4' of coaxial cable, it is best to build a solid dipole with at least #16 wire.

Receiver transmission lines

Receiver transmission lines sounds like a misnomer, and I suppose that it is in one sense. The term *transmission line* is used throughout this book. If you are a shortwave listener, it is likely that your antenna will do nothing more than feeding received signals to your radio. However, most of the antennas in this book can also be used by radio amateurs for receiving and transmitting. In these cases, the term *transmission line* is more accurate.

Although there are almost as many types of transmission line as there are portable antenna designs, only two are normally satisfactory for portable systems. They are the single-wire feeder and coaxial cable. As mentioned in previous chapters, the single-wire line can be the actual end of the element or a separate wire that is attached to the center or slightly off-center on the element. The latter method might be too complicated for easy storage and assembly because it tends to get wrapped around the antenna element. Specific lengths are often required for center or off-center fed single-wire lines, which can hinder the simplicity and convenience of these portable designs.

Coaxial cable transmission lines have a decided advantage in longevity and simplicity over the center-fed single-wire variety. The antenna element can be easily separated from the cable after storage, and any convenient length can be used for successful operation. One slight disadvantage of this type of cable is the weight. RG-

58U coaxial cable is the smallest variety commonly used with antennas. It can often be found on the government and industrial surplus markets at very reasonable prices for lengths of up to 1000'.

When purchasing cable for portable antenna systems, make certain that it is intended for outside use. Some brands and types of cables are intended to be used indoors only or within a sealed line of conduit. Moisture causes the indoor variety to become extremely inefficient after short periods of use because the insulation becomes "contaminated."

Other types of transmission lines can be used with portable antennas, but they usually become bothersome after a few uses. Twisted conductor lines soon become crushed and tangled after cramped storage. Twin-lead can become brittle and break after any substantial rough treatment, and spaced twin-conductor tuned lines will end up with broken insulators. These other varieties of transmission line are also more bulky and difficult to store in small compartments. Continuous use of these lines is almost impossible without complete replacement after several uses. Also, with these types of transmission lines, you need an antenna tuner to match the twin-feed lines to your receiver. A system like this is bulky and complicated—two qualities that are best avoided in a portable antenna system.

Compactness

If all of the rules have been followed so far, the portable antenna can be made into a small, easy-to-store bundle with very little effort. Simply coil the main antenna element into a convenient loop, then tie or tape the turns so they won't slip. If the antenna uses a center-connected transmission line, coil it in the same manner and secure with string, tape, or sandwich bag "twisties." Dipole antennas can be easily stored by forming three separate loops; one for the transmission line and the others for each of the two element segments (Fig. 9-1). The three loops can be placed on top of one another and taped into one large coil. Unpacking this portable system is easy. You only have to remove the tape, separate the loop into its three basic sections, and slowly uncoil the elements and the receiver transmission line.

Always allot time at the end of your shortwave-listening activities for careful collapsing, securing, and storage of the portable antenna system. Hasty packing could mean broken cable connections, twisting and bending of elements, and possible stretching of conductors. All of these factors shorten the useful life of a portable antenna, and turn a system that should last for years into a useless heap of wire (Fig. 9-2) in a short period of time. When careful planning and work are invested in an antenna project, equal care and planning are required to maintain it.

Weight

You will quickly discover the advantages of a lightweight antenna design if you must use it in a remote area that requires a long hike over rough terrain. The weight of the receiver, power supply, and other accessories are quite a burden, and a heavy antenna tossed in might be just enough to make the shortwave-listening aspect of the journey appear to be a waste of time. Antennas and all equipment intended for portable use *must* be as light as possible. As mentioned earlier, wind stress factors

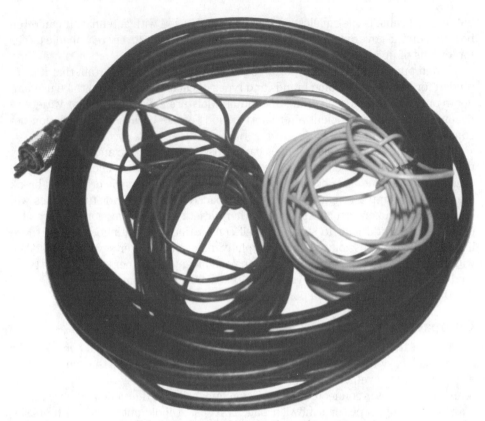

9-1 A dipole coiled into its three elements.

9-2 An unkempt antenna.

are lower when antennas are small in element diameter and weigh little. Obviously, high supports, even the collapsible variety, are impractical for many applications. Therefore, natural supports must be used most of the time to hold portable antennas in their proper mounting attitudes. Some trees have large branches that could support more than 100 pounds, but many have only thin or dead branches that can be used only for the lightest systems. When building any antenna designed for portable or spur-of-the-moment uses, always plan on a "worst case" mounting: one where poor supports, high winds, and rocky terrain prevail. If designed for this type of use, the system should perform well under typical mounting conditions, which are usually a bit better than the worst-case example.

As with conventional antennas, those designed for portable use sometimes have certain compromises when used primarily in areas or regions of the country that pose special problems. An area that receives higher-than-normal wind velocities for a major part of the year requires a stronger-than-normal antenna system. Larger-gauge element wire and heavier insulators help to fortify the antenna. Fortunately, regions with higher-than-normal wind speeds usually contain trees and other natural supports that are fortified against these weather conditions. These trees contain fewer thin weak branches and usually have thicker foliage to serve as anchoring points for antenna elements.

Extreme cold also affects antenna designs for portable use—especially when moisture occurs along with these low temperatures. Small-gauge wire has a tendency to become brittle and break when exposed to frigid weather conditions. Enamel-coated copper wire is not as vulnerable to ice buildup because droplets of water tend to fall from this slick surface immediately instead of adhering, as is the case with bare copper conductors. Even a small buildup of ice along the antenna element adds a great amount of weight and might break the antenna (Fig. 9-3).

You will have to deal with these and many other regional problems when designing the antenna system. Most of the construction projects in this chapter are suitable for the great majority of shortwave listeners. Those in areas with special problems might have to modify some of the designs for their particular use. By adhering to proper antenna design principles, you can significantly change many of these antenna construction projects while still maintaining an efficient system that operates properly.

Locations

Remember when putting up mobile antennas that the land you are setting up on is not yours (unless you live on a farm). Setting up could get you into a lot of trouble. Campgrounds and state and local land are some of the best locations for mobile antennas. Just make sure that you follow any rules and regulations that apply to this land. Some locations, such as rest stops and picnic areas along major highways, don't seem to have any set regulations; you should have no problems installing low-profile, temporary antennas on this land. A few definite no-nos would be to string an antenna across the road or to run wire about neck height across the path leading to the bathroom. Just use common sense.

Private land can be another problem. These days, many people are cautious about such things as lawsuits and drug deals. Installing an antenna on someone's

9-3 Snow built up on an antenna.

land, then sitting in your car for a few hours, could make someone suspicious that you are up to no good. On the other hand, you could be on the land of someone who is simply paranoid. Trespassing is a good way to get shot or to land in jail (the food is bad and the reception is even worse), so don't do it!

Portable grounds

If you have a portable, battery-powered shortwave receiver, you are better off not worrying about the subject of grounding equipment or antennas while you listen from a car. Because of the design of these receivers, you probably won't be able to recognize a difference between one that was grounded or ungrounded, so taking the time to install a ground would basically be a waste of time.

On the other hand, if you are serious about listening during a car outing and are taking a table-top receiver that can be operated from 12 volts, it might be a good idea to connect the ground terminal of the receiver to the body of the car. To do so, just cut a length of heavy gauge wire (normally about #8 to #12) to approximately 8' to 10' long. Solder a large alligator clip, such as the battery-charger types mentioned previously, onto one end of the ground wire (Fig. 9-4). Strip a few inches of insulation (if you use insulated wire) from the other end of the wire. Then, when you go out in the field to do some listening, just loop this end of the wire around the ground terminal of the receiver and connect the large alligator clip to the body of the car.

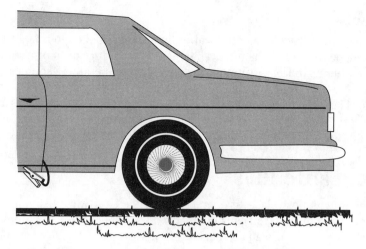

9-4 Using a large alligator clip to connect the ground to the car chassis.

If you are an amateur radio operator, the ground system is a key factor in whether your outing is successful. If you are using a common, commercially made whip antenna on your car, it would be worth your while to use a ground, rather than ground the shielded braid of the coaxial cable to the car. One of the best grounds under these circumstances is the counterpoise ground, such as the ones used for the quarter-wave vertical antenna projects in chapter 7. As described there, the counterpoise ground is simply a few quarter-wave elements that are located above the ground. The above-ground grounds are handy in this situation. Can you imagine burying and then removing a complete ground radial system or a few 6' ground rods every day that you plan to go out and operate from a car? Simply cut several quarter-wave wires from #12 to #16 stranded wire and attach them to the ground braid side of the whip antenna or coaxial cable. If you're in a remote location, you can just let the radials hang from the car to the ground (Fig. 9-5).

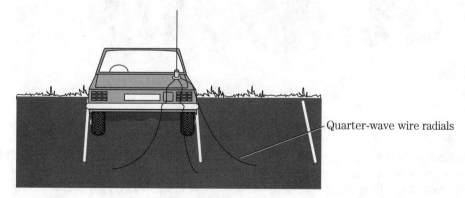

Quarter-wave wire radials

9-5 A counterpoise ground system connected to the receiver in a parked car.

Motor noise

When listening from a remote location in an automobile, you might decide to keep the engine running to maintain a charge on the battery or to provide heat during cold-weather operations. Automobile engines are sometimes a source of receiver noise that can range from slightly bothersome to completely impossible for receiver operations. The ignition systems in cars can cause a severe buzzing interference in most receivers. The only real measures to remedy the situation are to either turn off the engine of the car or to use a diesel car (which doesn't have spark plugs).

Vehicle antennas

Sometimes the best place to operate a portable shortwave listening station is from a parked automobile. You can obtain power from the cigarette lighter input jack on the dash, or you can use a portable battery-powered receiver. Or you might even have a car stereo that covers the shortwave bands, such as the Philips DC-777 (Fig. 9-6). In-car listening could be handy for shortwave listeners; not only is it a nice way to catch some radio signals if you live in a radio-hostile environment, but the car protects you from uncomfortable temperatures and precipitation.

9-6 The Philips DC-777 shortwave car receiver.

In fact, the car listening trip is an interesting idea for active DXers who want to catch some rare stations without spending a fortune, losing vacation days from work, or neglecting friends or family for long periods of time. Even if your home location is good for shortwave listening, you can probably find a better place somewhere else. For example, I have a fair homesite for shortwave antennas and my parents' home (which I occasionally visit) is excellent for listening. Still, I have had the urge to sneak out to the coast of New Jersey or Massachussets and point a huge longwire at Europe. Radio waves lose more energy when traveling over land than they do traveling over water. So, if you are attempting to hear low-power shortwave or mediumwave (AM broadcast band) radio stations from another continent, you are better off listening from the coast nearest to that continent.

Simple antennas

Under most circumstances, the simple wire antenna (or longwire) is the best choice for mobile listening in a parked car or truck. As with *the wire* in chapter 1, all you need to do is remove the insulation from one end of the wire and attach it to the antenna terminal or wrap it around the end of the whip antenna on the portable receiver. Then, run the wire out the window and keep going until you go reach the end and need to find a support to tie it to (Fig. 9-7).

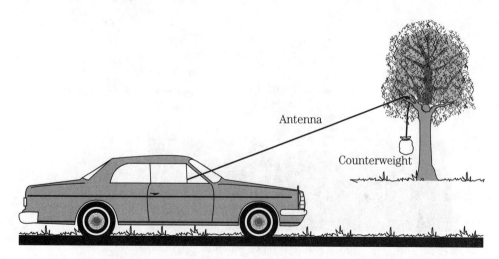

9-7 A random-length longwire hung in a tree.

As mentioned earlier in this chapter, very light-gauge wire, such as #26, is excellent to use as a simple longwire antenna. Wire with such a small diameter is easy to wind, can be wound into a very small ball, and is difficult to see. Another advantage is that you can run the wire out through your car window, and your window can still close. That little extra edge is important when it is 15° and you would otherwise be freezing to death with a ½" window opening and a length of coaxial cable running out the window!

The performance for this type of antenna is similar to the wires and longwires that are covered elsewhere in this book. Very long longwires are directional off the ends of the antenna. So, you should aim the wire at the direction that signal is coming from. Shorter longwires are less directional but are still fine for general listening excursions.

Car antenna extender

The automobile antenna can be used to feed the signal to the car shortwave receiver. An automobile antenna extension provides a means of lengthening the short whip that is supplied with most cars and trucks. You can lengthen this element to provide good shortwave reception (Fig. 9-8). The concept behind this antenna is similar to that behind clipping a longwire antenna to the whip antenna of a portable receiver. This concept is about as simple as any idea out there, and best of all, it works well.

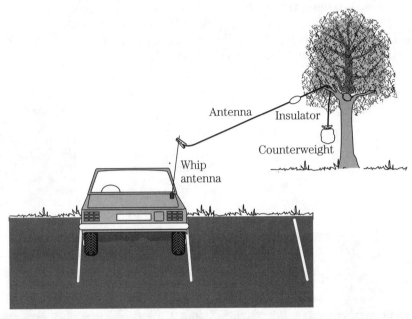

9-8 A simple car whip antenna extender.

The construction is quite simple. A length of #16 copper wire serves as the major part of the antenna element. Slip the far end through the eye of a small ceramic insulator, then wrap it and solder it at several points. Scrape all insulation from the section of wire to be soldered. Thread the other eye of the insulator with the short length of nylon clothesline rope and tie it. Fit the opposite end of the element wire with a heavy-duty alligator clip. A clip lead similar to that which is supplied with some battery chargers is ideal and it is strong enough to hang on under the strain of long antenna elements. This lead should be firmly attached to the alligator clip and soldered at several different points. If you choose a smaller gauge of wire, you should be able to, in turn, use a smaller size of alligator clip.

The antenna extender is now complete. With typical antenna element lengths, the entire system can be stored in areas as small as the glove compartment of most automobiles.

Choose a likely support for the far end of the antenna element and attach it firmly. Carefully extend the element wire to the automobile antenna and make a firm connection at this point with the alligator clip. For most portable receivers, you would be better off not connecting anything to ground—it's not worth your trouble.

This antenna is very simple and very efficient for portable operation. In addition to the usual caution about coming in contact with high-voltage lines, be certain that the *entire* system has been dismounted and stored before attempting to leave the portable operating location.

Longwire kite antenna

Portable antennas require some sort of tall mast or other object to support one or more ends of the antenna element. Some portable locations will be barren of trees or other high structures, making the installation of these antennas impossible. This problem can be circumvented by using the kite antenna, which requires only a moderate wind to commence operations.

This might seem like an unusual idea, but the kite antenna has been used successfully not only for receiving, but for transmitting radio signals. Antenna elements several hundred feet in length are quite feasible in areas where winds blow constantly. The height achieved at the far end of the antenna element can reach far above the 100' mark.

The longwire kite antenna consists of a small-gauge enamel-coated copper wire attached to a standard paper or plastic kite in place of the usual kite string (Fig. 9-9). The added weight of the copper wire might cause some difficulties in the initial launching procedure, but once airborne, the kite should perform well. Depending on wind conditions, wire gauges in the neighborhood of #22 to #26 should be sufficient. Stronger winds and larger kites might require a slightly larger gauge of wire. Wear gloves to prevent wire burns caused by sudden tugs of the airborne kite.

Make connections to the shortwave receiver in the usual manner; clip the end of the kite element to the antenna terminal, and attach the chassis ground connection to a stake driven at least 3' into the soil. If you are merely receiving and not transmitting, a good ground system is not necessary. However, a ground system usually provides better overall antenna efficiency. See the section on portable grounds earlier in this chapter for more information.

Choose an open area to launch the kite initially. Once it becomes airborne, stand as close to the receiver as possible while you unwind the antenna wire. When the kite is out an adequate distance, try to maneuver it in altitude until it reaches a layer of relatively stable wind flow that does not require constant attention from the operator on the ground to maintain correct height and control. Gusting winds will continually whip the kite around in the sky and might cause it to spin out of control and fall to earth just when that rare foreign station becomes readable.

When you have maneuvered the kite to a proper altitude and stability, wrap a section of the element wire around the wooden holding stake, which should be located no more than 1' from the receiver. You can then trail the remaining wire to the receiver. Then, cut it and connect it to the antenna input terminal.

Reception with this type of portable antenna system varies from poor to excellent as a result of the variations of wind velocities in different areas. Again, strong winds are not necessarily best for good operation. These conditions usually are periodic, lasting for only a few seconds at a time. This might force you to pay constant

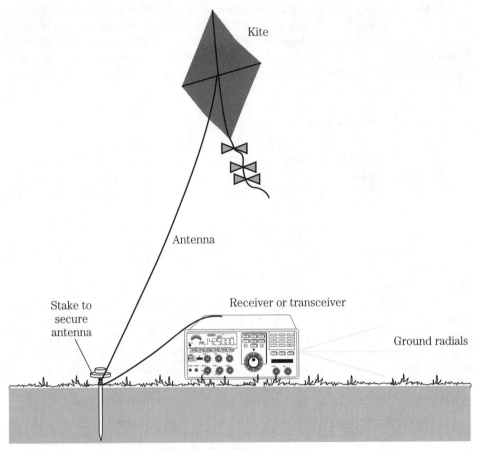

Kite

Antenna

Stake to
secure
antenna

Receiver or transceiver

Ground radials

9-9 A kite-mounted longwire antenna.

attention to keep the kite flying, instead of listening to incoming shortwave signals. When wind conditions are ideal, the kite antenna can outperform most other types, but when conditions are at their worst, operation is next to impossible. For this reason, you should choose the kite antenna for serious operation when you are in an experimental mood—not in life or death situations. Many shortwave listeners who enjoy portable operations carry along a kite antenna to be used only at times when wind conditions are ideal for this type of system. They depend on their standard portable antennas for most work, but are always on the lookout for conditions that will allow them to fly an antenna with an element several hundred feet in length.

The kite antenna should *not* be used in any area where electric high-tension wires are near. A kite with the standard twine control line is very dangerous when it crosses a high-voltage cable, but one with a copper conductor extending to the ground can be lethal. Another operating safety consideration is electric storms. Even if lightning has not been seen or heard in the vicinity of the kite, a nearby storm can charge the atmosphere for miles around and a high voltage can build up on the element. Do not attempt to operate this antenna system unless the weather is excellent and free from any type of electrical storm. If you disregard the signs of an upcoming storm, you could become a modern-day Ben Franklin—except with more fireworks and less fame and fortune.

The kite antenna can be altered to use other means of supporting the element at a distant point above the ground. Helium-filled weather balloons have been used in areas that do not have winds of sufficient velocity to allow the kite method to be used. Balloons are usually superior to kites for purposes of antenna support. However, only the large commercial or military designs are adequate for shortwave antenna purposes. These can sometimes be found in surplus catalogs and military outlet stores. Many come complete with their own helium inflation cylinders, but some of the older styles are equipped with a hydrogen generator to fill them. Hydrogen balloons are not safe for most applications. The gas is extremely flammable and difficult to contain and handle. These types of balloons should be bypassed for the later models, which are inflated with helium. As stated earlier, helium balloons are superior to average kites in terms stability and listening ease, but the balloons and the helium canisters can both be expensive. Check for prices and availability before you start this project.

High winds have adverse effects on balloon-supported antennas; the winds push balloons to the earth when they are secured to a ground point. Areas with little or very light wind conditions are best suited to this type of support system. Even greater heights and antenna element lengths have been obtained with balloon-supported systems. Because of the extra possible heights with these antennas, the hazards of electrical storms are even greater than with kite-supported antennas. Be careful!

10
CHAPTER

Directional antennas

Directional antennas are those that transmit and receive best in one certain direction and reject signals that approach from other directions. Directional antenna systems are especially handy for people who want to focus the capabilities of an antenna on one particular part of the world. These systems are the favorites of DX-ers (shortwave listeners who search for rare and low-powered stations) and amateur radio operators (who often need to focus their power on one particular direction so that all of the signal power travels toward the person that they are talking to—not the rest of the world).

Of all basic antenna designs, the directional antenna requires the most care and accuracy of measurements to be effective. It is usually difficult to design a directional system that offers a high degree of reception and rejection ability over a broad range of frequencies, such as those encountered when working the shortwave bands. Many radio amateurs find that it is necessary to construct several directional antennas, one for each shortwave band, to obtain a truly directional system for most shortwave frequencies. The problem is that the more directional an antenna is, the less it can receive signals from other directions. Thus, for lower frequencies, at least four antennas are necessary to receive signals from all directions. However, for many types of antennas, other arrays must be constructed for other frequencies. To install fixed, single-frequency directional arrays to cover all of the shortwave bands, you would have to own many acres that could be dedicated to holding masts, guy wires, and complicated systems of transmission lines. As a result, you almost never see fixed arrays of quad, delta, log periodic, or yagi antennas.

A directional antenna is best utilized when some means is provided for rotating the element or elements to the desired receiving directions. Again, this is not a large problem on the higher bands, but as the frequencies are lowered, size and especially weight become an almost insurmountable obstacle. Unfortunately, the expense of heavy-duty rotors, the space requirements, and the vertical support requirements usually prevent most average shortwave listeners from ever coming close to building a multielement directional antenna system for any frequencies lower than about 13 MHz.

If you believe that a directional antenna system might suit your needs, study each project in this chapter, then decide which one will be most useful to you and what will be most feasible in your available space. Whether you live in the center of a city or in a rural area, one of the practical directional antenna projects should fit in your allotted area for antenna "habitats."

Each project lists the element lengths and a parts list (where applicable), as well as a formula for determining element length. You should cut each element precisely to the correct length for the frequency desired. This same antenna will exhibit some directional properties on other frequencies, but performance in a directional sense will deteriorate proportionately with the amount of deviation from the design frequency length of the system. Fairly good omnidirectional operation should still be maintained on all frequencies lying above the proper operating frequency.

Several antenna elements can be stacked above each other. Each can be cut to operate on a different frequency, if you want to operate on several different bands. However, the antennas should be at least a quarter wavelength apart. Placing two horizontal elements in a horizontal plane with each other decreases the directional properties of both antennas. Considering the time, energy, and money that you have to spend getting these complex antennas into the sky, it seems silly to lose some of the directional characteristics because of carelessness.

The aluminum tubing dipole

The rotatable aluminum tubing dipole antenna (Fig. 10-1) takes advantage of the somewhat directional properties of the basic dipole antenna. The added advantage is that the entire system can be turned so that you can select the area from which reception is desired. To operate with true bidirectional properties, this antenna system must be mounted at least one half wavelength above the earth's surface or, if mounted over a metallic structure (such as a tin roof), at least one half wavelength above that. A closer mounting to the earth or other conducting surface interferes with the directional receiving patterns and causes the antenna to receive signals approaching it from a less perfect pattern—one that is less directional. Because of the complexity of this antenna and the fact that it is not especially feasible for the lower frequencies, it might be best used by amateur radio and citizen's band operators, who need to direct their signals toward the stations they want to talk to.

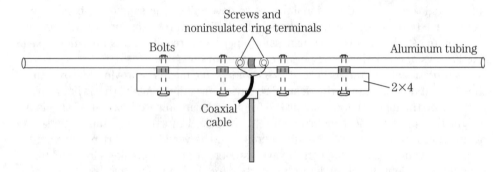

10-1 The tubing dipole.

Construction materials include two quarter-wavelength sections of aluminum tubing. Thin-walled electrical conduit 0.5" in diameter can be substituted, but aluminum tubing is lighter. That's a real advantage when at least 15' of tubing must be rotated on a mast.

The ¾" variety normally is available in 6' and 8' lengths. If the antenna that you are building is longer than the lengths of tubing available, you can saw one of these sections with a hacksaw, then attach each piece to the remaining two sections with a standard ¾" tubing connector. Make certain each connection is tight and secure to prevent future problems.

The two finished sections of tubing need to be bolted to a 2 × 4 to hold the antenna steady. Try using a 5'-long treated-lumber 2 × 4. The tubing needs to be bolted to, but insulated from, the 2 × 4. You can use insulators that can be bolted down, or you can substitute pieces of rubber to stand off from the board and insulate the tubing. Then, drill two holes about 2' apart at one end of each tubing. You will bolt the tubing to the 2 × 4 at these places. Hold each section of tubing against the 2 × 4 at the location where it will be permanently attached and mark through each hole with a pencil. Also mark the location for another hole, at the center (lengthwise and widthwise) of the 2 × 4. Then, drill the holes in the 2 × 4 and weatherproof it with paint, varnish, or polyurethane. Attach the insulators, and bolt the tubing to the 2 × 4.

Drill a small hole at the end of the tubing pieces that are facing the inside (the center of the 2 × 4). This hole should only run through the top "side" of the tubing—not through the complete diameter of the tubing. Prepare the coaxial cable in the same manner that you would prepare it for a standard dipole antenna (see the section on dipole antennas in chapter 7). Depending on how far apart you have the elements spaced, you might need to allow an extra inch or two of center conductor and braided shield in order to reach the holes in the top of the tubing. Next, run the end of the coaxial cable with the two stripped wires through the hole in the center of the 2 × 4. Solder a noninsulated ring terminal (available in many different sizes from Mouser Electronics, 12 Emery Ave., Randolph, NJ 07869) to the end of the center conductor and to the end of the twisted shielded braid of the coaxial cable. Then, bolt each ring terminal through one of the holes in the antenna elements. This connection must be tight or it will corrode slightly, and the antenna will be very inefficient. Finish the joints by wrapping everything with electrical tape from the end of the coaxial cable to the screwed-in ring terminals. This measure prevents weather from damaging the connections and the coaxial cable.

To begin mounting the antenna, screw a pipe flange to the underside of the 2 × 4 so that it matches the hole through the center of the board (string the coaxial cable through it). Then, pick up a steel pipe section from a hardware store to serve as the mast. Choose the pipe flange and the pipe so that they match in diameter. A 1" diameter pipe should be fine for the purpose. The length of the pipe depends on whether you want the antenna to be turned by hand or by a rotor.

Even if you are on an extremely tight budget, the rotor is almost certainly the best choice. With the decline of off-air reception for television programs, you can often pick up working rotors for free. If this is the case, the pipe that connects to the antenna needs only to be about 4' to 10' long. Install the antenna and mast as you would for a standard television antenna.

In order to install a mast that you can turn by hand, run the coaxial cable through the pipe and screw the pipe tightly into the flange. This prevents the cable from becoming twisted around the mast. You can use bracket-type mounting clamps or U-bolts to connect the mast to the side of the house. As long as the clamps or bolts aren't too tight, you will be able to turn the pipe/antenna by hand. Other types of mounting hardware provide a shallow well, or seat, for the bottom of the pipe to rest in and a clamp. Use ample amounts of heavy-duty car grease to reduce friction at these two heavy-wear areas. The holding support rods that are screwed or bolted to the window frame should be short enough to allow easy access so that you don't have to lean out too far. For better turning leverage, either clamp a handle to the side of the pipe or drill and bolt a handle on. This method of antenna rotation is sometimes referred to as the *armstrong method*, for obvious reasons.

Troubleshooting

The rotatable dipole antenna is one of the simplest forms of rotary-beam antenna construction. If built properly, it will work well, but a defective coaxial cable transmission line or improperly soldered or connected joints at the center of the element can cause failure. Make the cable checks before the antenna is erected, because it is much easier to check it on the ground than it is to check it in the air.

Maintenance

Periodically examine this antenna system to ensure continued safe operation. If you notice any sign of aging or breaking down in the wooden support, take down that section and immediately replace it. High wind conditions can cause metal fatigue after continued use, so periodically examine (on the ground) the elements and the mast. Be certain to closely inspect the couplers (if used) that join the two parts of each element section. Look for signs of looseness or fatigue. Replace them if you have any doubt about their structural integrity.

The 1" pipe should be able to withstand any normal high-wind conditions the average shortwave listener is likely to experience, but if you notice *any* signs of bending in this section, replace it. Once a support pipe is bent, it continues to bend under high-stress conditions and eventually drops the entire antenna system it supports. Always consider the safety of persons who might be walking beneath the antenna when mounting any potentially dangerous structure.

A 2-element beam antenna

Like all antennas, it is possible to create variations that are particularly useful in some given situation. For example, the directional characteristics of the dipole antenna can be further emphasized with the use of reflector or director elements. These elements are especially handy on a rotatable beam antenna because the pattern of best reception or transmission can be aimed at the point where it is most effective. Fixed multielement beams are much less useful because they are basically only good in one direction. This is fine if you only care to "work," or hear, one particular region of the world, such as the northern part of South America, but lousy if you have interests around the globe.

The theoretical differences between a 2-element beam (Fig. 10-2) and a rotatable dipole are very small. Just toss on an extra element to direct signals back to the dipole and you're set. However, the system becomes complicated in real life because you need to find a way for the director element to stay in the air and for the whole array to be balanced and mounted to a mast. That can be difficult. In fact, the 2-element beam antenna is very difficult for the beginner to build and install. Because of the weight of the wood and the large wind area that it could provide, it is best to keep this one small. Also, you must check with the local authorities to see what sorts of antenna arrays are legal in your town or city. The array as described here might not be legal in your area. Also because the local building inspector might be able to provide you with some ideas to improve your installation, you should certainly talk to the local authorities before starting to build anything of this sort. One last major warning: *Under no circumstances should you ever put the beam antenna in a location where it or the mast that it rests on could contact power lines.*

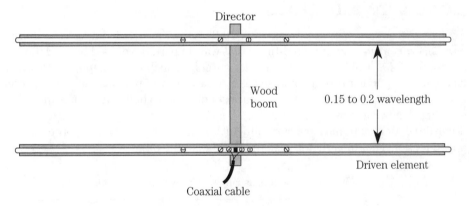

10-2 The 2-element beam antenna.

The only difference between the instructions for the rotatable dipole and the 2-element beam is that the wood that supports the beam should be a bit lighter; try 2-×-2 treated lumber instead.

In this type of system, some of the names and rules about antennas seem to change. For example, with beam antennas, the dipole element of the antenna is now known as the *driven element* because it is connected to the transmission line. Also, some parts of the antenna are not even connected to the transmission line. The director is so named because it merely directs signals to the driven element (in the case of receiving) or it directs signals away from the driven element (in the case of transmitting).

Because the director is not directly fed by the transmission line, it is known as a *parasitic element*. Thus the director can be one long piece of tubing or several that have all been properly secured together. This element can then be mounted on a piece of 2 × 2, as described in the section on the rotatable dipole antenna. To find the length of the director element, multiply the length of the driven element by 0.96. Your element will be 4% shorter than the driven element.

These two elements need to be spaced approximately 0.2 to 0.25 wavelength apart, and you need to connect these two elements together so that they can be rotated at the same time. This means that the two antenna elements that have been attached to 2 × 2s in turn need to be installed on a *boom*. This boom should be a treated-lumber 2 × 4 that has been weatherproofed with paint, varnish, or polyurethane. Bolt the elements onto the boom at a distance of 0.2 to 0.25 wavelength away from each other. To further strengthen the two antenna elements on the boom, cut four diagonal cross bars and bolt them to the boom and to the wooden antenna element supports.

This entire boom should be securely mounted in the center with bolts. Like the rotatable dipole, the 2-element beam antenna can be rotated with a rotor, but it is best not to try the "armstrong method" of turning this antenna, unless you have a strong arm and a penchant for frequently opening the window no matter what weather conditions are like.

Longwire antennas

The classic *longwire antenna* (Fig. 10-3), sometimes called a *wave antenna* or a *Beverage antenna*, is an old-timer that was, in part, developed by H. H. Beverage in the 1920s. Unlike some of the older antennas, such as the zepp, the longwire has remained popular throughout the years for a variety of reasons. As stated earlier in this book, the longwire is one of the easiest antennas to build, and it has the effect of being somewhat directional. It is very beneficial for the beginner, because most other directional antennas are very difficult to build. The longwire is probably the only directional antenna that is easier to build than the dipole.

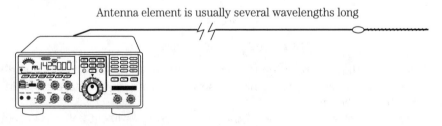

Antenna element is usually several wavelengths long

10-3 A simple longwire antenna.

The longwire is simply one long piece of wire, in a relatively straight line, that is connected to a receiver at one end. If electrical noise is a problem in your household, prepare a length of coaxial cable to reach from your receiver to the point at which your antenna will start to head off in a straight direction from your listening post. Twist and solder the center conductor of the coaxial cable to the antenna element. Then, twist and solder the shielded braid to a wire that will connect to a ground stake or a ground system.

It is best to use a thicker gauge of wire for the longwire, otherwise there will be some losses in signal strength. However, the antenna is so large that lack of signal strength probably will not be a problem, but the cost of several hundred or thousand feet of #14 copper wire might prevent you from ever wanting to build a longwire. For my nonpermanent longwires, I normally use #26 enamelled wire, and I have been very successful.

Unlike most other antennas, reception by the longwire is not especially negatively affected by its proximity to the ground. In fact, some cold-climate DXers string a few thousand feet of wire across the snow in preparation for a big weekend of DXing. The normal height for a receiving longwire is about 8' off of the ground: low enough that it is easy to string, but high enough that no one will be "clotheslined" by the wire. For transmitting/amateur radio work, it's best to keep the antenna as high as possible so that the signal radiating from the antenna won't be mostly absorbed by the surface of the earth.

An interesting effect of the longwire antenna is that the longer it is, the more directional it is off the ends of the antenna. If these patterns could be seen from above, they would look like two very large lobes heading off in opposite directions. The longer the antenna is, the greater the gain and the smaller the width of the lobes. Because of the large signal strengths, the longwire is of the best antennas to use when trying to hear a tiny signal from a distant country. Because of the very directional properties of this antenna, it is also a favorite for mediumwave (AM broadcast band) DXers, who use these properties to "null out" strong stations that are on either side of the wire. And the more wavelengths long the antenna is, the tighter the lobes become and the more directional the antenna becomes. However, after the antenna becomes several wavelengths long, some of the smaller lobes that are perpendicular to the two main lobes become stronger. These minor lobes negate the nulling effects of the longwire that are so important at mediumwave frequencies. I guess that it's just as well anyway; a four-wavelength long antenna at 540 kHz would be 7289' long!

Mediumwave listeners often use a resistor and a ground at the end of the antenna to make the longwire even more directional (Fig. 10-4). "Terminating" the antenna in this manner allows the antenna to receive signals well only from the far end—not from both ends. To terminate the end of a longwire, solder a 600-Ω carbon-composition resistor at the end of the antenna, then solder enough wire at the end of the resistor to reach the ground. The ground should be either a standard 4' or 6' ground stake or a buried radial system. As stated earlier, you probably won't want to terminate the longwire if you are listening to shortwave, because the shortwave bands aren't filled with nearly as much interference as the mediumwave band.

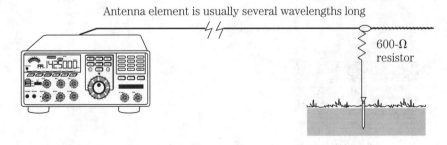

Antenna element is usually several wavelengths long

600-Ω resistor

10-4 A terminated longwire antenna.

One advantage of the longwire is that it works well at most frequencies, whether receiving or transmitting although, compared to other antennas, the longwire is best at lower frequencies. A 308' long half-wavelength longwire cut for 1600 kHz performs well from that frequency and up through the bands. This antenna also performs quite well even on the FM band and on television frequencies. Longwire antennas are rarely used at these frequencies because at that many wavelengths, they won't null out stations as well as a yagi or a log periodic. And more importantly, you can't hit a button and turn your longwire!

The V antenna

The *V antenna* (Fig. 10-5) is really two longwire elements coupled together at an angle that makes the two complementary in receiving efficiency. The V-beam is bidirectional and the main receiving area is located through the center of the angle between the two elements. The V antenna is ideal for the rural shortwave listener who has the amount of space available to contain a structure of this size. Construction is very simple, so don't let the overall bulk of this project alarm you. If space is available, you can probably complete the V antenna in one or two weekends.

The V antenna is interesting because it has even more gain than the single longwire antenna. Like the longwire, the V antenna can be lengthened almost infinitely to improve directional receiving and transmitting performance. As you might have guessed, the pattern for reception and transmission for the V antenna is two lobes that run through the middle of the V: Each originates at the feed point of the antenna.

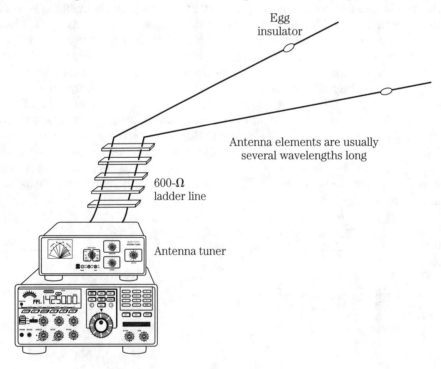

Egg
insulator

Antenna elements are usually
several wavelengths long

600-Ω
ladder line

Antenna tuner

10-5 A V antenna.

To build the V antenna, string out two longwires and solder each one to a length of 600-Ω ladder line (transmission line). Connect the ladder line to an antenna tuner, which you should connect to your receiver. You could terminate the end of each leg of the V. I'm not positive what effect this would have on the pattern of reception and transmission, but I assume that it would only work well from one direction: that which is coming in from right between the two grounded ends.

The longwire/V array

Now it's time to have some fun with V and longwire antennas. Up until this point, the only advantage that the V antennas have over longwires is a slight bit of signal strength. Big deal; that little bit of signal strength won't make that much of a difference—not considering the extra amount of work that you have to put into that extra leg. The real fun begins when you construct about six or seven longwires and have the choice of using any single antenna alone or using several in conjunction as a V antenna. The big advantage here is that the V antenna has a different receiving pattern than the longwire antenna. By having six switchable longwires, you actually have about 10 or more reception patterns to choose from. This is possibly the only case where you can effectively wind up with more antennas than you actually built.

To build this longwire/V array, you need at least an acre or two of land behind your house. That requirement alone eliminates many people from trying the longwire/V array. You need about six or seven longwire antennas that are arranged in about a 170° pattern (Fig. 10-6). Because of the bidirectional effects of the unterminated longwire antennas, this arrangement effectively covers radio signals arriving from any direction.

For the antenna elements, use a wire gauge that's no lighter than #22. With all of the stress that will be on the antennas, it's best to use stranded wire rather than solid wire, which can break under constant flexing. The V elements should all be run like standard longwires, except make sure that you leave a few extra feet at the receiver end of the antennas. Attach one fairly large screw eye to the house (near the window of your radio room) for each antenna element. Also use an egg strain insulator between each screw eye and each antenna element. Tie about 1' of nylon cord between the screw eye and the egg insulator (Fig. 10-7). Then, run the antenna element through the other side of the egg insulator and allow at least enough antenna element wire to make it inside your window. The amount of leftover wire varies, depending on where you want to place the antenna junction box in your radio room. If you used insulated wire, peel off several inches of wire on either side of the insulator. Now that the wire is bare, twist it together and solder the joint at this place. Depending on how you want the antenna wires to run into your house, it is a good idea to use insulated wire from the egg insulators by your house to the antenna junction box. That way, you can bundle the wires up without having to worry about them shorting together.

Bundle the wires together with a few cable ties and drill an adequate hole through the window frame. Be careful that you don't drill into any nails or electrical wires! Run the wires through this hole and also run your ground wire from a ground stake through this hole. Then, seal it up with weatherproof caulking.

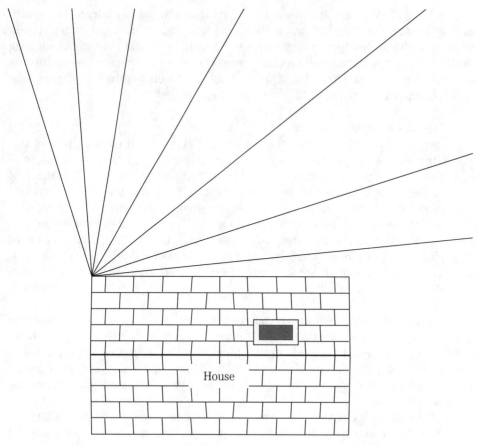

10-6 A V/longwire system (from above).

Next, you need an antenna junction box (Fig. 10-8). The keys to this box are a project box and a flat board of jacks, such as the types used in the back of stereos and stereo mixers. Cut a hole in the front of the project box, then screw in the board of jacks. Drill one hole in the back of the box that is large enough for the bundle of antenna elements to pass through. Solder each antenna element to the center of a different jack. Solder all of the outside (shield) connections of the jacks together. Cut a hole in the back of the project box for a screw terminal to fit in. Then, solder a wire from all of the ground wires to this terminal. Now, you can connect your ground wire to the outside of this terminal.

You now need a handful of plugs, some alligator clips, and some shielded microphone wire. The bare minimum for this system would be two cables of each, but you might want to make a few more for experimental purposes or in case you lose a cable. Considering that most of these jack boards use ¼" RCA plugs, I'm assuming that those are the types that you used. It doesn't matter what type you used so long as you purchased matching plugs. Strip a proper amount of insulation from each end of the microphone wire. Solder the center conductor of the wire to the center of the

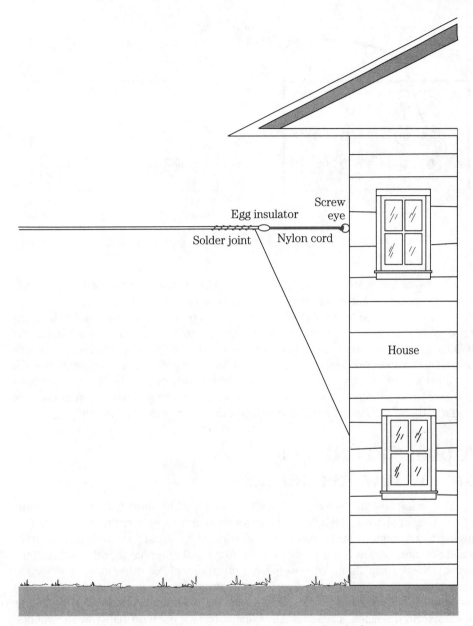

Screw eye
Egg insulator
Solder joint   Nylon cord

House

10-7 V/longwire antenna elements mounted to the house.

plug and the outer braid to the outside of the plug. At the other end, cut the ground shield off and solder the center of the wire to the alligator clip. Then, you can attach these alligator clips to your antenna tuner.

An alternate method would be to screw SO-239 jacks to the front of the project box and make a Y-adapter out of coaxial cable and PL-259 connectors. Then, the connector can be screwed directly into your receiver. This method is a bit more dif-

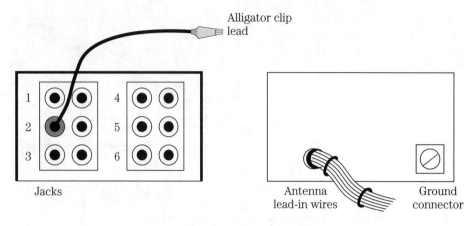

10-8 The connector box for the V/longwire system.

ficult to make and a little bit more expensive. Also, I'm not positive what sort of effect the impedance mismatch would have on your reception.

This longwire/V antenna system works great. I consider it to be about the best antenna system that you can own without dedicating more than 10 acres and thousands of dollars to your antenna. Best of all, it is cheap and relatively easy to build. I experimented with a stripped-down version of this system clipped onto the whip antenna of a portable receiver. In some cases, the one leg worked better than the other. Sometimes the other leg was better. Once in a while, reception was best when both antennas were used together. That kind of flexibility and directionality is rare in an antenna!

A phased vertical array for the low frequencies

Horizontal antenna elements are impractical for many shortwave listeners below a frequency of about 13 MHz. Vertical antennas require less horizontal space, and, if guying requirements can be met, they offer many hobbyists a solution to a directional antenna system on the lower bands. A vertical antenna, for all practical purposes, receives signals equally well from all approaching directions. If a second vertical element is added, true directional characteristics can be obtained in a limited space. Vertical beams are available on today's commercial market for the higher shortwave frequencies. These usually consist of two or more half-wave elements. When using grounded vertical elements, the height of the element above ground only needs to be a quarter wavelength because (as was mentioned earlier) the earth itself makes up the other half of the antenna.

A phased vertical array can be made electronically rotatable by adding other elements and complicated switching networks, but this project deals with only a basic design, which receives signals with excellent directivity from one general direction only. A study of the terrain in your area and the direction of stations that you wish to receive determine the best direction to align your antenna array. Many of the components used in this project are critical, and substitutions are not recommended. The larger and more expensive RG/8 coaxial cable is used in construction of this array because each type of coaxial cable has a velocity characteristic rating that is slightly different. This rating is essential to establishing the proper length of phasing cables to be used. If a smaller variety was substituted, the various lengths would have to be changed for proper operation. This type of antenna array actually delays a portion of the signal from one of the antennas, and the velocity factor rating is a measurement of the amount of delay for each type of coaxial cable.

A good radial grounding system is a must for this directional antenna system. Each vertical radiator must have its own individual ground network for good operation. If excellent ground conductivity is present in the soil where the antennas are to be erected (a situation that very rarely exists), a long metal stake (driven five or more feet into the ground) might be adequate. For most hobbyists, a network of ground wires buried beneath the soil is necessary.

Another must for construction of this project is a relatively clear, open area for an antenna site. Surrounding metal objects cause the directional pattern to become distorted and, in severe cases, completely useless. Make certain your chosen site is as near perfect as possible before taking on a project of this size. Close tolerance to element lengths is also necessary because of their dependence on one another. Each element should be exactly the same length and the same height above the ground. Their grounding systems should also be very similar. This is a very sophisticated directional antenna system, one which requires more time, patience, and money to erect than others covered in this chapter, but the overall receiving results are well worth the extra effort.

Using the lengths provided in Fig. 10-9, this array receives well from 7 to about 8 MHz. A wider range of effective reception can be had with the use of an antenna coupler between the receiver and the transmission line, although directional characteristics begin to decay above 8 MHz.

A coaxial T-connector is used in the phasing line and is available at most hobby and radio stores. The cable ends that connect to this adapter should be fitted with PL-259 coaxial plugs, as should the receiver transmission line. The length of coaxial cable from the T-connector back to the receiver location is not critical and the most convenient length can be used. There will be an excess (about 60') of coaxial cable between the two antennas. This cable can be coiled and taped for a neater and safer arrangement. The large coil can then be taped to a small stake or buried. Coiling this phasing line has no noticeable effect on the operation of the vertical array.

The antenna elements can be constructed of aluminum tubing isolated from ground on ceramic insulators and guyed with clothesline rope, or they can be lengths of #12 copper wire held up by wooden supports. Conveniently spaced trees can also be used as overhead supports without much distortion of the directional receiving patterns. Grounded metal supports are not recommended.

Tuning this system is not particularly difficult if you take proper care to measure the elements and the phasing lines. Simply connect the receiver transmission line to the center of the T-adapter and run it to the receiver or matchbox. Peak the antenna trim control (if your radio has one) on your receiver for maximum response on a weak signal, and the system is operational. You can check the directional character-

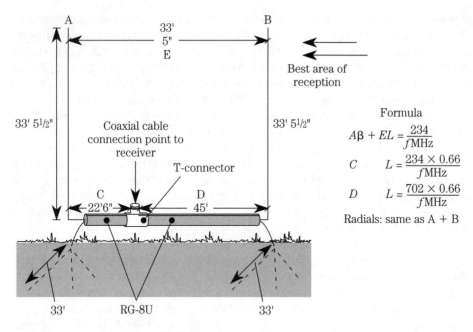

10-9 The phased vertical array.

istics of this antenna by switching rapidly between this and an omnidirectional antenna. The directional array has the ability to receive signals from one general area while canceling out those that arrive from other directions. This antenna should provide quieter reception by canceling out static and unwanted signals from areas other than the desired direction.

Troubleshooting

Problems with an array of this design are almost always associated with the coaxial cable phasing line or a break in the receiver feed system. An ohmmeter shows an infinite resistance when connected to the receiver end of the transmission line. A lower reading indicates a short. Remove the receiver feed line from the T-connector and measure it again. If the low reading is still present, the short is in this line. If an infinite reading is obtained, the short lies somewhere in the phasing network. The transmission line can now be reconnected, and one section of phasing line can be disconnected at a time until the problem cable can be identified. Do not attempt to repair any cable faults. Complete replacement is the only solution for this array, which depends heavily on the length and quality of the coaxial cable for proper operation. A break that is repaired can change the velocity factor of the line, which would result in poor or inefficient operation from the system as a whole.

Alterations

This directional vertical array can be easily converted to exhibit its directional properties in the opposite direction from what was originally its prime coverage area by simply reversing the phasing line. Connect the longer line to antenna A and the shorter one to B. The directional receiving ability has now been reversed a full 180°. By installing several more elements around one of the antennas at the proper distances and by switching in other phasing lines, an electronic type of rotation could be possible for an entire 360° circle. However, a system of this magnitude would be very costly and require a very large open area.

By using the formula provided, the directional array can be designed to cover any of the frequencies in the shortwave bands. But because of the work and materials needed, it is much more practical to consider another type of directional antenna for use on the higher frequencies, where great element lengths are not required.

The loop antenna

The *loop antenna* (Fig. 10-10) is a truly odd creature that seems to fly in the face of everything that you know about the way that standard antennas behave. The loop is theoretically a very complicated antenna that consists of several loops of wire wrapped around a box or a box-like form. The loop antenna is useful because it is very directional—it receives best from either end of the box form and it has very deep nulls broadside to the antenna. As a result, the loop isn't particularly useful on the shortwave frequencies, where there is little adjacent-channel interference, but it is an excellent choice on the mediumwave band, where many frequencies rumble with the noise of many stations broadcasting at the same time.

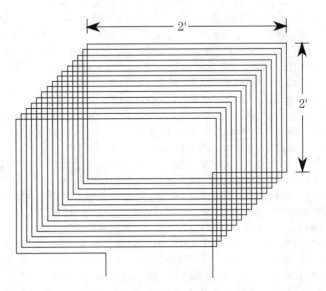

15 turns of wire spaced ¼" apart

10-10 A wire coil design for the mediumwave broadcast band.

Because of the extremely directional characteristics and the very small size of loop antennas, they obviously have some great advantages. Of course, like any other type of antenna, they also have drawbacks. Probably the worst drawback is that they have such a small signal pickup that most people connect them to an amplifier so that the signals are strong enough to hear. Because of the low signals, the performance isn't as hot as a long longwire, V, or rhombic antenna, but many people don't have enough room for these antennas anyway.

This section is intended merely to give you a glimpse at the loop antenna and encourage you to try one for yourself. Loop antennas are so complicated that whole books have been written on the subject. Rather than dig into the theory of loop antennas, this section provides a working example of a loop antenna for the mediumwave broadcast band.

As I said earlier, the loop antenna is much different in theory than other antennas. When I built my first loop, I assumed that I could increase the signal pickup by adding more turns of wire to the antenna, the idea being the same as for the longwire antenna—more wire equals bigger signal and equals more points at which the antenna is resonant. I also believed that more wire would make the antenna more directional. Such is not the case. I found a 2' × 2' box and wrapped 120 turns of #26 wire around it. When I tested the antenna, I found that it received poorly in all directions. I thought that the household wiring or other metallic objects might have been skewing the directional characteristics of the antenna, so I shielded it by wrapping almost the whole thing in aluminum foil until it looked like a 1950s-era science fair project. It still received about on par with a 10' piece of wire. What was the problem?

Like Chumley and Tennessee Tuxedo, who visited Dr. Whoopee when troubles arose, I called a technically inclined friend. Much to my surprise, I found out that loop antennas only operate on the frequency that they are cut for; they do not operate at harmonic frequencies (multiples of the wavelength). So, the antenna that I had labored over for hours was useful only for receiving in the VLF band. The frequency was so low that I probably wouldn't have been able to hear much more than the plates of the earth shifting, etc. How depressing!

To build a loop antenna for the mediumwave broadcast band, you first need a coil form. Although loop coil forms can be most any size, the one in this project is 2' × 2'. I wound my ugly prototype around a cardboard box, but you might want to build a nice-looking coil form out of wood (Fig. 10-11). Simply cut a wooden base and drill a hole in the center of it. Cut a 1" diameter 1.5' long dowel rod to fit into this hole. Or, if you want to be more decorative, try an approximately 1.5' long lathe-turned piece of a chair or banister. Then, cut two 2.83' long pieces of wood to be used as crossbars. Drill a hole through the center of these and through the top of the wood that is attached to the base. Bolt the crossbars on and drill holes through the ends of the crossbars. Then glue dowel rods into these crossbar holes. You can build the AM loop with either 15 turns of wire that are spaced ¼" apart or you can use 19 turns of wire that are spaced ½" apart. Whichever way you choose, mark the locations of the turns on the dowels with a pencil and cut light grooves with a hacksaw. This way, the wire spacings will remain even and the wire will be secure on the coil form. Now, apply finish to the coil form.

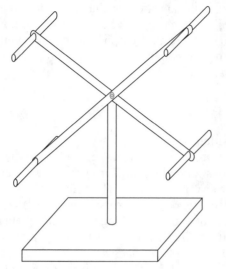

10-11
The loop antenna wooden
coil form.

Wrap the wire around the dowel rods. Leave enough extra wire at each end to reach the base easily. Tape these ends to the base. Now, purchase a 365-pF variable capacitor, also known as a *broadcast variable*, and mount it in the center of the base. These capacitors are commonly used as tuning controls in standard AM radios. Solder these two wires to the variable capacitor, then solder a length of coaxial cable to the capacitor. The capacitor enables you to tune the loop antenna over the entire (hopefully) mediumwave band. Solder a standard PL-259 connector onto the end of the coaxial cable so that you can plug the loop into your receiver. If you own a portable receiver with an antenna jack on the side, solder a plug on that matches (probably an ⅛" plug).

As stated earlier in this section, the loop antenna should receive best from either end of the coil. Signals to the broadside of the loop should basically disappear. A number of problems can occur with a loop, but the two most common are a distorted receiving pattern and a lack of full coverage across the broadcast band. My 120-turn monstrosity had absolutely no directional characteristics because it was made for a much lower frequency than I was using it on. Another cause of distorted reception is using the loop inside a metal-structured building, such as a trailer, motel, or metal shed. To alleviate the problem, wrap all but one 2" gap at the top with aluminum foil. This solution is really ugly, so if it works, you might want to try coaxial cable around the coil form instead of wire. The only difference would be that you should remove the outer jacket and the shielded braid for a 2" gap across the top of the loop.

As for the loop not tuning across the entire band, try adding more wire (if you want to reach the bottom of the band) or removing some wire (if you want to reach the top of the band). Another solution would be to make the entire coil variable. To do this, first make sure that the loop easily tunes to the bottom of the broadcast band (540 kHz). Don't solder the one wire of the loop to the capacitor; instead, attach a 1' long lead to the capacitor with an alligator clip on the "free" end. Remove the insulation (if you used insulated wire) from a small ½" strip across the loop. Then, connect the alligator clip to the unattached wire of the loop. If the antenna won't properly tune up to 1600 kHz, remove the alligator clip and attach it to the next-to-last wire on the loop. By doing so, you electrically remove one of the turns of the loop, and it should tune to the top of the band. By using this method, you can also use the loop into the shortwave bands, although it will probably stop being useful at about the 31-meter shortwave broadcast band.

Conclusion

You can see from the information provided and the construction details and drawings that directional antenna systems for shortwave operation closely resemble their undirectional counterparts. Most directional antenna systems are composed of several dipoles, longwires, or quarter-wave verticals. The combining or stacking of these basic antennas affects the electrical performance and causes certain receiving areas on the antenna to be phased out while increasing the receiving ability of another area of the antenna. The different basic sections act exactly as they would if mounted alone, as would be the case with a single half-wave dipole. This separate action is combined when several antennas are "stacked" to form an overall *antenna system*. This antenna system performs differently than any of the separate parts.

Directional antennas are not for the individual who prefers a haphazard and informal method of building projects. Each detail is very important and a minor mistake could result in a complete malfunction in directional operations. The average shortwave listener does not have the sophisticated electronic measuring devices required to determine the efficiency of a directional antenna, so you must strictly adhere to proven designs and measurement to be certain that you are installing the best receiving system possible.

11
CHAPTER

Radio interference

The shortwave listening hobby has one great advantage over other communications hobbies. Interference to televisions, radio receivers, and other types of electronic equipment is not caused by listening to a shortwave receiver. Ham radio operators, especially in weak television reception areas, are often plagued by reports of their transmitters causing TVI (television interference). In most instances, this type of interference lies not in the transmitter operating at frequencies other than those permitted, but by a lack of filtering in the receiving device. Some radios and television sets, as well as stereos, electronic ignition systems, and even electronic garage door openers, present an alarming lack of resistance to strong radio frequency transmissions. Proper shielding and bypassing of circuits would eliminate a majority of interference problems, but this work must be done to the devices themselves and not to the ham transmitter.

Shortwave listening interference comes from the electrical noise and hum of appliances, car ignition noise from passing trucks and automobiles, and a wide range of other electrical equipment that produces noise in the shortwave receiver. As stated earlier, much of the problem might lie within the receiver itself. Even the most expensive receiver on the market might lack immunity from some of the noises mentioned, but a little work on the part of the hobbyist can clear up some problems.

Broadcast station interference

One of the most common interference complaints is caused by a strong local AM broadcast station that seems to broadcast a strong signal at every tuning point on the shortwave receiver dial. The cause of this problem is the intensity of the broadcast signal; at close range, it bypasses or jumps the frequency-determining parts in the receiver and enters the audio circuits where it is amplified for reproduction through the speaker or headphones.

The only cure for this condition is to find a way to reduce the strength of the radio signal at the receiver, which can be easily and inexpensively accomplished by using a trap at the receiver antenna input connections. The trap is made in the same way as the ones made for some of the shortwave antenna projects, but the capacitor and coil are tuned to the frequency of the interfering broadcast station. The trap allows all signals to pass on to the receiver except those that are transmitted at the frequency for which it is tuned; in this case, the broadcast station. Signals at this frequency are effectively conducted to ground so no interference can reach the receiver. In severe cases, all of the interfering signal might not be eliminated, but a marked improvement usually occurs.

Figure 11-1 shows a schematic for a trap for the AM broadcast frequencies. The unit is built inside an aluminum box, which must be attached to the receiver. It is important that this box be grounded to the receiver chassis, which is in turn connected to the ground system. Two connectors are fitted to the metal box and should match the connector supplied with your receiver for connection to the antenna transmission line. A miniature toggle switch is connected between the conductor, which passes from connector to connector, and the trap. This switch inserts the trap into the antenna circuit when you push it to the *on* position and removes it when you push it to the *off* position. Keep the coil and capacitor as close to the center of the aluminum box as possible to prevent any detuning effects. Once the broadcast filter has been completed, install it in the antenna circuit at the receiver antenna input terminal, and adjust the iron core tuning element of the coil with a small screwdriver. Adjustment is correct when the interfering station drops out of the receiver speaker completely or reaches a low point and then begins to rise again.

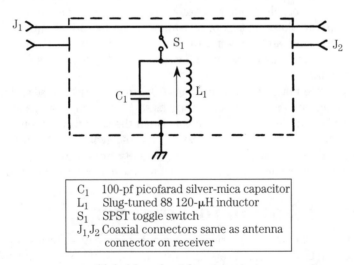

C_1	100-pf picofarad silver-mica capacitor
L_1	Slug-tuned 88 120-μH inductor
S_1	SPST toggle switch
J_1, J_2	Coaxial connectors same as antenna connector on receiver

11-1 A broadcast frequency trap.

When two or more stations cause interference to the shortwave reception, other traps can be built in the same manner and each tuned to reject one interfering signal. All traps can be mounted in one large aluminum box with adequate clearance provided for the individual coils. Three separate switches are also required to connect the traps in and out of the antenna circuit to the receiver. When properly built, a broadcast filter should not interfere with reception of other stations in the broadcast band except those that lie in close proximity to the frequency being grounded by the trap. If the receiver is moved to another location, where a different interfering broadcast station is present, it is a simple job to retune the trap to the frequency of that station; the broadcast filter is a useful device to mount permanently on the chassis of the shortwave receiver. Table top receivers, not portable models, work well with this arrangement, and the device can be transferred to a different model with no retuning required.

Noise interference

Several types of noise can adversely affect the receiving performance of a shortwave radio. Some is inherent in the receiver itself and can get worse when the tubes (if any) begin to get weak. The other types of noise emanate from industrial electric equipment and automobiles. This type of noise is usually heard at the receiver in two forms. One is a sudden crack (or several cracks) of high volume for short durations of time. The other is a hiss, which continues for several seconds and can build in volume and then gradually fade away. The sharp and sudden noise is usually caused by a spark discharge, which is generated when an electric appliance or light switch is turned on. The hiss type of noise could be caused by an electric motor running on the ac line to which the receiver is connected or is nearby, fluorescent lights, a leaky power line transformer, etc.

Receiver tube noise can be eliminated in many instances by replacing the defective tubes and having the circuitry checked for any breaks or shorts. I realize that tubes have been outdated for 30 years, but a great number of tube receivers are still in use. Receiver hum can be the result of a bad electrolytic capacitor in the power supply. Replacing the capacitor usually brings reception back to a normal level of sensitivity. Improperly soldered connections in the receiver circuitry might cause popping or cracking noises, much like those encountered when a spark outside the receiver is produced. A good way to check if the noise problem is in the receiver or not is to listen on a similar receiver in the same operating position and using the same antenna system. If the noise is still heard on the second receiver, then the problem lies somewhere else. If the interference disappears, then a future examination of receiver circuitry is in order. This test is not 100% foolproof because two different shortwave receivers might respond differently to noise or they both could have the same problem. However, the check is worth a try and might determine the problem immediately—especially if the receivers are of similar design.

One possible cure for receiver noise that is produced outside the unit itself is to install a very good ground system, which is then connected to the receiver chassis. Vertical antennas with buried wire radials provide an automatic ground when connected to the receiver antenna input, but if a very long receiver transmission line is used, the resistance of the ground conductor could reduce the overall grounding efficiency. A separate ground rod can be located near the receiver and a separate connection can be made to this point. Dipole antennas and other systems that provide no earth grounding are most likely to benefit from a separate chassis ground.

Front-end overload

Sometimes a received shortwave signal is so strong that it causes distortion in the speaker or headphones. In receivers that are equipped with an *RF gain control*, some of this problem can be eliminated by turning it to a lower setting. This reduces the receiver's sensitivity to incoming shortwave signals. Severe cases of front-end overload can render this control and, for that matter, other receiving circuits, useless for good reception. A solution to this problem is to install a device called an *attenuator* between the antenna and the receiver.

An attenuator differs from the trap mentioned earlier in that it is not tuned to any specific frequency, and it attenuates or reduces all incoming signals. A switch is supplied on most units for quick removal of the additional circuits from the antenna input during reception of weaker signals, which need the full sensitivity of the receiver to be heard properly. Most attenuators are built with several levels of signal reduction, which can be varied by switching in or out of different electronic circuits.

Now many receivers (even portable receivers, which are especially susceptible to front-end overload) contain built-in attenuators. Most of them carry different names, such as "AM RF gain control." Either way, it's an attenuator and it helps reduce or prevent front-end overload.

About 10 years ago, I had one of the less-expensive table-top/portable receivers that had recently gone out of production. For a while, I used a random wire antenna, then I decided to "graduate" to a real antenna—a dipole. Although it was true that I could hear many more stations, about half of them were receiver images. In effect, I could "hear the same number of stations on twice as many frequencies." After that, I stopped using the dipole and went back to the random wire. It is a bit disheartening to build a "hot" antenna, only to find that your receiver can't handle it. Sometimes the best and easiest solution is to give up and go back to your old antenna . . . or buy a new receiver!

TV receiver interference

Some television sets can cause a kind of interference to the shortwave receiver because of signal radiation. This radiation can come directly from the local oscillator of the TV receiver or even from the ac power line to the set. When the radiation comes directly from the picture tube, it is usually an indication that the television receiver has defects that should be serviced by a qualified technician.

Antenna radiation can be cured by installing a device made from coils and capacitors called a *high-pass filter*. These units are sold for a few dollars on the commercial market and are often used to prevent interference *to* the television by amateur and citizen's band transmissions. The third type of radiation interference, which is generated over the power cord to the television, can be eliminated by connecting a 0.01-μF disc capacitor from each conductor of the cord to the chassis ground of the set. Most television sets of modern design do not present this problem, but if you suspect this type of interference, you can easily check by monitoring the shortwave receiver while turning the set on and off. If the interference comes and goes with the television on/off switch, the trouble lies in this area.

Television interference to shortwave receivers is rare—especially when proper antenna installations are made. Keep all antenna elements and cables as far as possible from any ac power wiring and connect the shortwave receiver chassis to a good grounding system.

Interference from a television receiver generally occurs on a set that is located very close to the shortwave antenna system, but severe cases of radiation can affect entire neighborhoods. FCC regulations state that the owner of a television receiver that is radiating excessive signals is responsible for its proper operations. He or she should be advised in a nice way that this set might be operating improperly. He or she can then take steps to correct the situation. Television sets, stereos, radios, and almost any electrical or electronic equipment can cause different types of interference when circuits become old or are out of adjustment. Arcing of electrical currents can occur, which might produce a hum, static, clicks, and noise in the shortwave receiver. Fortunately, most of these types of interference are weak. Often the offending device is in the same building as the receiving system and can be more easily hunted down.

Natural interference

Another type of interference is totally natural and thus often difficult, if not impossible, to eliminate. This interference can be caused by weather conditions, differences in sunspot cycles, and even meteor showers. These natural forms of interference often come unexpectedly and vanish in the same manner. Some remain during the hours of daylight and are never experienced at night. Natural interference stems from a wide range of conditions that might encompass the entire world, a single continent, or even a small area of a country. Very little can be done about this interference other than to install an adequate amount of noise-canceling devices at the shortwave receiver. Noise limiters and blankers do an admirable job of clearing the receiver of much or all of these extraneous signals.

The ionosphere

Shortwave listeners who have been active for years sometimes feel that their antennas or receivers are beginning to lose efficiency because of the deteriorating reception of signals from certain parts of the world and on specific bands and frequencies. Although deterioration of the listening equipment could be a factor (primarily if you have a tube receiver), changes in sunspot activity might be the real cause. The ionosphere, a charged layer in the earth's upper atmosphere, plays an important role in signal reception on frequencies that lie in the shortwave band. Its makeup is changed daily, weekly, monthly, and yearly by the condition of the sun and the number of sunspots. Ionospheric activity is determined by the amount of radiation that the ionosphere receives from the sun. This ultraviolet radiation changes in cycles that are determined by the earth's rotation, the sun's rotation, the 11-year sunspot cycle, magnetic storms, upper atmospheric conditions, and other extraterrestrial disturbances. Any condition that affects the ionosphere will probably have some effect on shortwave frequencies and will render some of them almost useless for varying periods of time.

Ionospheric changes are sometimes gauged by a factor that is abbreviated as *MUF, maximum usable frequency*. It determines the highest frequency that is reflected back to earth by the ionosphere during present conditions. The MUF changes with sunspot activity, seasonal differences, and time of day. As the maximum usable frequency drops, the higher frequencies in the shortwave spectrum become increasingly poorer for reception over longer distances. Groundwave reception, which is composed of signals that do not strike the ionosphere, but travel within the lower atmosphere, is not so dramatically affected by some of the changes mentioned.

When a signal is transmitted at a frequency higher than the MUF, it simply penetrates the ionosphere and travels out into space, and only groundwave reception can be maintained for any distance. Daily changes can cause a frequency that is marginally close to the MUF to be usable for long-distance reception during the daylight hours and completely useless when the sun drops below the horizon. On the other side of the world, this frequency can start to become active for the rest of the day.

Sunspot cycles

The 11-year sunspot cycle is the factor that has the greatest effect on ionospheric conditions and thus on shortwave reception. During the peak, reception from the far corners of the world can be maintained on frequencies from 11 MHz and above during day and night hours. As the peak begins to decline these higher frequencies become less and less active, while the lower frequencies (between 2 and 10 MHz) start to open up for contacts at longer distances. When the sunspot cycle reaches its minimum, these lower frequencies might be the only ones open for nighttime listening, and the upper areas of the shortwave band are completely inactive, some during both the day and night. Approximately every 11 years, one full sunspot cycle is completed, and shortwave listeners run the gamut from easy signal reception to extremely difficult, and everything in between. This is not to insinuate that it is useless to listen in on the high frequencies during a sunspot ebb. Other conditions can cause these portions of the shortwave band to become suddenly active and open to communications to all parts of the world. These openings often vanish as quickly as they come, but a great deal of productive listening can be accomplished over a period of hours, days, or weeks when the band is open.

The sunspot cycle was near maximum during October 1989. Already the higher frequencies have begun to deteriorate. Still, shortwave listening could be very productive for you, depending on what stations you are trying to hear. For example, although the bottom of the shortwave cycle spells big problems for DXers, program listeners still have no problem catching the latest from most of the European countries, Radio Canada International, HCJB, and many others. Shortwave charts are available from many sources that list the times, frequencies, and dates of the most favorable conditions. Information is also provided as to which countries are open to reception at specific times and on which specific frequencies. Though primarily intended for amateur radio operators, these charts can provide a wealth of information to the average shortwave listener. Some organizations even offer a phone-in service that can be dialed at any time for the latest information on shortwave conditions and openings. These reports are more timely than the published version.

Summary

This chapter has dealt with interference, the ionosphere, the sun, and the parts they each play in the generation of noise in the shortwave receiver. The analyzing of interference should be an easier task when this information is applied to specific problems. Always ascertain the source of the noise *before* attempting any means of corrections. Too many fruitless hours have been spent bypassing circuits only to find that the true source of the interference was a change in the upper atmosphere, unusual weather conditions, or the neighbor's lawnmower. Too often the policy of "act now—think later" is applied by the eager enthusiast. It can cost a good deal of money. Time and money should only be invested in areas where increased listening satisfaction is the result. When troubleshooting interference problems, a hasty plan of action often rewards the individual with the return of the original problem—only many hours and dollars later.

Approach all interference problems on a step-by-step basis. Ask yourself questions (just don't do it out loud in public). Does the interference occur at any particular time of the day? Has it progressed from a slight annoyance to a real problem over a long period of time? Do other SWL friends report the same noisy conditions? These and other questions should be asked before you make a decision about what is causing the interference. Once the cause has been determined, then you can find the solution and correct the problem.

This step-by-step advice applies in all areas of the hobby. Never be so certain of the causes of problems associated with shortwave listening that the proper tracing and analyzing of the situation seems completely unnecessary. By thinking out every problem, much more time can be devoted to the fun aspects of this interesting hobby. This advice does not mean that experimentation should not be attempted. By all means experiment at every opportunity, but keep your projects within the lines of correct basic procedures and practices. Don't attempt to solve a problem by saying "There are 15 different possibilities for the correct solution, so I'll start with number one and keep going until the right one is found!" Instead, reason out the nature of the problem. Careful study can eliminate many of the possible corrective measures until only two or three remain. Then, apply your reasoning and test your analysis by trying the solutions that have not been eliminated. Much time, effort, and money can be saved if each project, problem, or experiment is carried out in this manner. Your skill and ability as a shortwave enthusiast will improve on a regular basis, and your overall enjoyment of the hobby will continue to increase.

A
APPENDIX

Wire lengths for half-wavelength antennas

To determine the total length of a standard half-wavelength ($\lambda/2$) antenna (such as a dipole), use:

$$l \text{ (length in feet)} = \frac{468}{f \text{ (frequency in MHz)}}$$

Each leg of the half-wavelength dipole antenna or the vertical element of a quarter-wavelength vertical antenna can be determined by dividing the length from the previous equation by two:

$$l \text{ (length in feet)} = \frac{234}{f \text{ (frequency in MHz)}}$$

Remember that the whole number from your calculation is in feet, but the remainder (every digit to the right of the decimal) is not in inches. Multiply the remainder by 12 to find the remaining inches.

For example, if you wanted to find the entire length of a half-wavelength dipole that is resonant at 7415 kHz, use:

$$l \text{ (length in feet)} = \frac{468}{7.415}$$

$$l \text{ (length in feet)} = 63.1153' \quad 0.1153 \times 12 = 1.383"$$

$$= 1" \text{ (rounded off)}$$

$$l \text{ (length in feet)} = 63' \ 1"$$

Because the dipole consists of two equal-length segments, divide the total length by two for the length of each wire.

$$l \text{ (leg length in feet)} = 63.1153'/2$$

$$l \text{ (leg length in feet)} = 31.5576' \quad 0.5576 \times 12 = 6.6918"$$

$$= 7" \text{ (rounded off)}$$

$$l \text{ (leg length in feet)} = 31' \ 7"$$

Of course, this is the difficult way. To avoid the mathematics, you can use the rough guide of the following table to construct antennas. It covers all of the short-wave frequencies, from 1600 to 30000 kHz. Early on, the steps are only 25 kHz apart, later it hits 50 kHz, and the spacing finally reaches 100 kHz apart. Why the variable spacing? The difference between the lengths of dipoles cut for 1600 and 1700 kHz is nearly 20', but the difference between the length of dipoles cut for 29900 and 30000 kHz is less than 1"! Thus, I felt a few extra steps would be helpful for anyone working with antennas on the lower frequencies.

Also, because the measurements rarely fall on an exact inch, they are all rounded off. As a result, the two quarter-wavelength "legs" that make a dipole add up to slightly longer than the antenna is supposed to be (according to the length in the second column). That's okay; if your antenna is ½" longer than the exact length found from an equation, you won't notice the difference. And if not being exact bothers you, work from the equation.

Most shortwave broadcast bands or amateur bands are approximately 500 kHz wide. Generally, the most effective and efficient method for building these antennas is to cut the antenna for the center of the band. For example, the 40-meter amateur band runs from 7000 to 7300 kHz, but American broadcast stations can be heard up to slightly above 7500 kHz. If you want to hear these stations, one antenna cut for 7250 kHz should work adequately. However, unless you use a log periodic or a discone antenna for the shortwave frequencies (very improbable!), you should limit your frequency ranges per antenna to 500 kHz or less. For various reasons, simple antennas are not capable of covering vast frequency ranges effectively.

In the following table, both amateur and broadcast bands are screened; where the bands overlap each other, a darker screen is used.

Frequency	Total length (λ/2 antenna)	Length per side	
1600 kHz	292' 6"	146' 3"	
1625 kHz	288'	144'	New top end of mediumwave (AM)
1650 kHz	283' 7"	141' 3"	broadcast band
1675 kHz	279' 5"	139' 8"	
1700 kHz	275' 4"	136' 7"	
1725 kHz	271' 4"	135' 7"	
1750 kHz	267' 5"	133' 8"	
1775 kHz	263' 7"	131' 9"	
1800 kHz	260'	130'	
1825 kHz	256' 5"	128' 2"	
1850 kHz	252' 11"	126' 6"	
1875 kHz	249' 7"	124' 9"	
1900 kHz	246' 4"	123' 2"	160-meter amateur band
1925 kHz	243' 1"	121' 6"	
1950 kHz	240'	120'	
1975 kHz	237'	118' 6"	
2000 kHz	234'	117'	

2025 kHz	231' 1"	115' 6"
2050 kHz	228' 4"	114' 2"
2075 kHz	225' 6"	112' 8"
2100 kHz	222' 9"	111' 5"
2125 kHz	220' 3"	110' 1"
2150 kHz	217' 7"	108' 9"
2175 kHz	215' 2"	107' 6"
2200 kHz	212' 8"	106' 4"
2225 kHz	210' 4"	105' 2"
2250 kHz	208'	104'
2275 kHz	205' 8"	102' 9"
2300 kHz	203' 6"	101' 8"	
2325 kHz	201' 4"	100' 7"
2350 kHz	199' 2"	99' 7"
2375 kHz	197'	98' 6"
2400 kHz	195'	97' 6"	*120-meter broadcast band*
2425 kHz	193'	96' 6"
2450 kHz	191'	95' 6"
2475 kHz	189' 1"	94' 6"
2500 kHz	187' 3"	93' 7"
2525 kHz	185' 4"	92' 7"
2550 kHz	183' 6"	91' 8"
2575 kHz	181' 9"	90' 10"
2600 kHz	180'	90'
2625 kHz	178' 4"	89' 2"
2650 kHz	176' 7"	88' 4"
2675 kHz	175'	87' 6"
2700 kHz	173' 4"	86' 8"
2725 kHz	171' 8"	85' 10"
2750 kHz	170' 3"	85' 1"
2775 kHz	168' 7"	84' 4"
2800 kHz	167' 2"	83' 6"
2825 kHz	165' 8"	82' 9"
2850 kHz	164' 3"	82' 2"
2875 kHz	162' 9"	81' 4"
2900 kHz	161' 5"	80' 8"
2925 kHz	160'	80'
2950 kHz	158' 8"	79' 4"
2975 kHz	157' 5"	78' 8"
3000 kHz	156'	78'
3025 kHz	154' 8"	77' 4"
3050 kHz	153' 5"	76' 9"
3075 kHz	152' 3"	76' 2"
3100 kHz	151'	75' 6"
3125 kHz	149' 9"	74' 10"
3150 kHz	148' 7"	74' 4"
3175 kHz	147' 5"	73' 8"

3200 kHz	146' 3"	73' 2"	
3225 kHz	145' 3"	72' 7"	
3250 kHz	144'	72'	
3275 kHz	142' 11"	71' 6"	*90-meter broadcast band*
3300 kHz	141' 9"	70' 11"	
3350 kHz	139' 8"	69' 10"	
3400 kHz	137' 8"	68' 9"	
3450 kHz	135' 8"	67' 9"	
3500 kHz	133' 9"	66' 10"	
3550 kHz	131' 10"	65' 11"	
3600 kHz	130'	65'	
3650 kHz	128' 3"	64' 2"	*80-meter amateur band*
3700 kHz	126' 6"	63' 3"	
3750 kHz	124' 10"	62' 5"	
3800 kHz	123' 2"	61' 7"	
3850 kHz	121' 7"	60' 9"	
3900 kHz	120'	60'	*75-meter broadcast band*
3950 kHz	118' 6"	59' 3"	*(Europe)*
4000 kHz	117'	58' 6"	
4050 kHz	115' 6"	57' 8"	
4100 kHz	114' 2"	57' 1"	
4150 kHz	112' 9"	56' 5"	
4200 kHz	111' 5"	55' 8"	
4250 kHz	110' 2"	55' 1"	
4300 kHz	108' 10"	54' 5"	
4350 kHz	107' 7"	53' 9"	
4400 kHz	106' 4"	53' 2"	
4450 kHz	105' 2"	52' 7"	
4500 kHz	104'	52'	
4550 kHz	102' 10"	51' 5"	
4600 kHz	101' 9"	50' 11"	
4650 kHz	100' 8"	50' 4"	
4700 kHz	99' 7"	49' 9"	
4750 kHz	98' 6"	49' 3"	
4800 kHz	97' 6"	48' 9"	
4850 kHz	96' 6"	48' 3"	
4900 kHz	95' 6"	47' 9"	*60-meter broadcast band*
4950 kHz	94' 6"	47' 3"	
5000 kHz	93' 7"	46' 9"	
5050 kHz	92' 8"	46' 4"	
5100 kHz	91' 9"	45' 10"	
5150 kHz	90' 10"	45' 5"	
5200 kHz	90'	45'	
5250 kHz	89' 2"	44' 6"	

5300 kHz	88' 4"	44' 2"
5350 kHz	87' 6"	43' 9"
5400 kHz	86' 8"	43' 4"
5450 kHz	85' 10"	42' 11"
5500 kHz	85' 2"	42' 7"
5550 kHz	84' 4"	42' 2"
5600 kHz	83' 6"	41' 9"
5650 kHz	82' 10"	41' 5"
5700 kHz	82' 2"	41' 1"
5750 kHz	81' 5"	40' 8"
5800 kHz	80' 8"	40' 4"
5850 kHz	80'	40'
5900 kHz	79' 4"	39' 8"	
5950 kHz	78' 8"	39' 4"	
6000 kHz	78'	39'	
6050 kHz	77' 4"	38' 8"	*49-meter broadcast band*
6100 kHz	76' 8"	38' 4"	
6150 kHz	76' 1"	38' 1"	
6200 kHz	75' 6"	37' 9"	
6250 kHz	74' 10"	37' 5"
6300 kHz	74' 3"	37' 2"
6350 kHz	73' 9"	36' 10"
6400 kHz	73' 2"	36' 7"
6450 kHz	72' 7"	36' 3"
6500 kHz	72'	36'
6550 kHz	71' 5"	35' 9"
6700 kHz	69' 10"	34' 11"
6750 kHz	69' 4"	34' 8"
6800 kHz	68' 10"	34' 5"
6850 kHz	68' 4"	34' 2"
6900 kHz	67' 10"	33' 11"
6950 kHz	67' 4"	33' 8"
7000 kHz	66' 10"	33' 5"	*40-meter amateur band*
7100 kHz	65' 11"	32' 11"	
7200 kHz	65'	32' 6"	*41-meter broadcast band*
7300 kHz	64' 1"	32' 1"	
7400 kHz	63' 3"	31' 7"	
7500 kHz	62' 5"	31' 3"
7600 kHz	61' 6"	30' 9"
7700 kHz	60' 9"	30' 5"
7800 kHz	60'	30'
7900 kHz	59' 3"	29' 7"
8000 kHz	58' 6"	29' 3"
8100 kHz	57' 9"	28' 10"

8200 kHz	57'	28' 6"
8300 kHz	56' 5"	28' 3"
8400 kHz	55' 9"	27' 10"
8500 kHz	55'	27' 6"
8600 kHz	54' 5"	27' 3"
8700 kHz	53' 9"	26' 11"
8800 kHz	53' 2"	26' 7"
8900 kHz	52' 6"	26' 3"
9000 kHz	52'	26'
9100 kHz	51' 5"	25' 8"
9200 kHz	50' 10"	25' 5"
9300 kHz	50' 4"	25' 2"
9400 kHz	49' 9"	24' 11"	
9500 kHz	49' 3"	24' 7"	
9600 kHz	48' 9"	24' 5"	*31-meter broadcast band*
9700 kHz	48' 3"	24' 2"	
9800 kHz	47' 9"	23' 10"	
9900 kHz	47' 3"	23' 7"	
10000 kHz	46' 10"	23' 5"	
10100 kHz	46' 4"	23' 2"	*30-meter amateur band*
10200 kHz	45' 11"	22' 11"	
10300 kHz	45' 5"	22' 9"	
10400 kHz	45'	22' 6"	
10500 kHz	44' 7"	22' 3"	
10600 kHz	44' 2"	22' 1"	
10700 kHz	43' 9"	21' 10"	
10800 kHz	43' 4"	21' 8"	
10900 kHz	42' 11"	21' 6"	
11000 kHz	42' 7"	21' 3"	
11100 kHz	42' 2"	21' 1"	
11200 kHz	41' 9"	20' 11"	
11300 kHz	41' 5"	20' 8"	
11400 kHz	41' 1"	20' 6"	
11500 kHz	40' 8"	20' 4"	
11600 kHz	40' 4"	20' 2"	
11700 kHz	40'	20'	
11800 kHz	39' 8"	19' 10"	*25-meter broadcast band*
11900 kHz	39' 4"	19' 8"	
12000 kHz	39'	19' 6"	
12100 kHz	38' 8"	19' 4"	
12200 kHz	38' 4"	19' 2"	
12300 kHz	38' 1"	19'	
12400 kHz	37' 9"	18' 10"	
12500 kHz	37' 5"	18' 9"	

12600 kHz	37' 2"	18' 7"	
12700 kHz	36' 10"	18' 5"	
12800 kHz	36' 7"	18' 3"	
12900 kHz	36' 3"	18' 2"	
13000 kHz	36'	18'	
13100 kHz	35' 9"	17' 10"	
13200 kHz	35' 5"	17' 9"	
13300 kHz	35' 2"	17' 7"	
13400 kHz	34' 11"	17' 6"	
13500 kHz	34' 8"	17' 4"	
13600 kHz	34' 5"	17' 2"	
13700 kHz	34' 2"	17' 1"	*22-meter broadcast band*
13800 kHz	33' 11"	16' 11"	
13900 kHz	33' 8"	16' 10"	
14000 kHz	33' 5"	16' 9"	
14100 kHz	33' 2"	16' 7"	
14200 kHz	32' 11"	16' 6"	*20-meter amateur band*
14300 kHz	32' 9"	16' 4"	
14400 kHz	32' 6"	16' 3"	
14500 kHz	32' 3"	16' 2"	
14600 kHz	32' 1"	16'	
14700 kHz	31' 10"	15' 11"	
14800 kHz	31' 7"	15' 10"	
14900 kHz	31' 5"	15' 8"	
15000 kHz	31' 2"	15' 7"	
15100 kHz	30' 12"	15' 6"	
15200 kHz	30' 9"	15' 5"	
15300 kHz	30' 7"	15' 4"	
15400 kHz	30' 5"	15' 2"	
15500 kHz	30' 2"	15' 1"	*19-meter broadcast band*
15600 kHz	30'	15'	
15700 kHz	29' 10"	14' 11"	
15800 kHz	29' 7"	14' 10"	
15900 kHz	29' 5"	14' 9"	
16000 kHz	29' 3"	14' 8"	
16100 kHz	29' 1"	14' 6"	
16200 kHz	28' 11"	14' 5"	
16300 kHz	28' 9"	14' 4"	
16400 kHz	28' 6"	14' 3"	
16500 kHz	28' 4"	14' 2"	
16600 kHz	28' 2"	14' 1"	
16700 kHz	28'	14'	
16800 kHz	27' 10"	13' 11"	
16900 kHz	27' 8"	13' 10"	
17000 kHz	27' 6"	13' 9"	

17100 kHz	27' 4"	13' 8"	
17200 kHz	27' 3"	13' 7"	
17300 kHz	27' 1"	13' 6"	
17400 kHz	26' 11"	13' 5"	
17500 kHz	26' 9"	13' 4"	
17600 kHz	26' 7"	13' 4"	
17700 kHz	26' 5"	13' 3"	*16-meter broadcast band*
17800 kHz	26' 4"	13' 2"	
17900 kHz	26' 2"	13' 1"	
18000 kHz	26'	13'	
18100 kHz	25' 10"	12' 11"	*17-meter amateur band*
18200 kHz	25' 9"	12' 10"	
18300 kHz	25' 7"	12' 9"	
18400 kHz	25' 5"	12' 9"	
18500 kHz	25' 4"	12' 8"	
18600 kHz	25' 2"	12' 7"	
18700 kHz	25'	12' 6"	
18800 kHz	24' 11"	12' 5"	
18900 kHz	24' 9"	12' 5"	*15-meter broadcast band*
19000 kHz	24' 8"	12' 4"	
19100 kHz	24' 6"	12' 3"	
19200 kHz	24' 5"	12' 2"	
19300 kHz	24' 3"	12' 1"	
19400 kHz	24' 1"	12' 1"	
19500 kHz	24'	12'	
19600 kHz	23' 11"	11' 11"	
19700 kHz	23' 9"	11' 11"	
19800 kHz	23' 8"	11' 10"	
19900 kHz	23' 6"	11' 9"	
20000 kHz	23' 5"	11' 8"	
20100 kHz	23' 3"	11' 8"	
20200 kHz	23' 2"	11' 7"	
20300 kHz	23' 1"	11' 6"	
20400 kHz	22' 11"	11' 6"	
20500 kHz	22' 10"	11' 5"	
20600 kHz	22' 9"	11' 4"	
20700 kHz	22' 7"	11' 4"	
20800 kHz	22' 6"	11' 3"	
20900 kHz	22' 5"	11' 2"	
21000 kHz	22' 3"	11' 2"	
21100 kHz	22' 2"	11' 1"	
21200 kHz	22' 1"	11'	*15-meter amateur band*
21300 kHz	21' 12"	10' 12"	
21400 kHz	21' 10"	10' 11"	

21500 kHz	21' 9"	10' 11"	
21600 kHz	21' 8"	10' 10"	*13-meter broadcast band*
21700 kHz	21' 7"	10' 9"	
21800 kHz	21' 6"	10' 9"	
21900 kHz	21' 4"	10' 8"	
22000 kHz	21' 3"	10' 8"	
22100 kHz	21' 2"	10' 7"	
22200 kHz	21' 1"	10' 6"	
22300 kHz	20' 12"	10' 6"	
22400 kHz	20' 11"	10' 5"	
22500 kHz	20' 10"	10' 5"	
22600 kHz	20' 8"	10' 4"	
22700 kHz	20' 7"	10' 4"	
22800 kHz	20' 6"	10' 3"	
22900 kHz	20' 5"	10' 3"	
23000 kHz	20' 4"	10' 2"	
23100 kHz	20' 3"	10' 2"	
23200 kHz	20' 2"	10' 1"	
23300 kHz	20' 1"	10' 1"	
23400 kHz	20'	10'	
23500 kHz	19' 11"	9' 11"	
23600 kHz	19' 10"	9' 11"	
23700 kHz	19' 9"	9' 10"	
23800 kHz	19' 8"	9' 10"	
23900 kHz	19' 7"	9' 9"	
24000 kHz	19' 6"	9' 9"	
24100 kHz	19' 5"	9' 9"	
24200 kHz	19' 4"	9' 8"	
24300 kHz	19' 3"	9' 8"	
24400 kHz	19' 2"	9' 7"	
24500 kHz	19' 1"	9' 7"	
24600 kHz	19'	9' 6"	
24700 kHz	18' 11"	9' 6"	
24800 kHz	18' 10"	9' 5"	
24900 kHz	18' 10"	9' 5"	*12-meter amateur band*
25000 kHz	18' 9"	9' 4"	
25100 kHz	18' 8"	9' 4"	
25200 kHz	18' 7"	9' 3"	
25300 kHz	18' 6"	9' 3"	
25400 kHz	18' 5"	9' 3"	
25500 kHz	18' 4"	9' 2"	
25600 kHz	18' 3"	9' 2"	
25700 kHz	18' 3"	9' 1"	
25800 kHz	18' 2"	9' 1"	*11-meter broadcast band*
25900 kHz	18' 1"	9'	
26000 kHz	18'	9'	
26100 kHz	17' 11"	8' 12"	

26200 kHz	17' 10"	8' 11"
26300 kHz	17' 10"	8' 11"
26400 kHz	17' 9"	8' 10"
26500 kHz	17' 8"	8' 10"
26600 kHz	17' 7"	8' 10"
26700 kHz	17' 6"	8' 9"
26800 kHz	17' 6"	8' 9"
26900 kHz	17' 5"	8' 8"	
27000 kHz	17' 4"	8' 8"	
27100 kHz	17' 3"	8' 8"	*Citizen's band*
27200 kHz	17' 2"	8' 7"	
27300 kHz	17' 2"	8' 7"	
27400 kHz	17' 1"	8' 6"	
27500 kHz	17'	8' 6"
27600 kHz	16' 11"	8' 6"
27700 kHz	16' 11"	8' 5"
27800 kHz	16' 10"	8' 5"	
27900 kHz	16' 9"	8' 5"	
28000 kHz	16' 9"	8' 4"	
28100 kHz	16' 8"	8' 4"	
28200 kHz	16' 7"	8' 4"	
28300 kHz	16' 6"	8' 3"	
28400 kHz	16' 6"	8' 3"	
28500 kHz	16' 5"	8' 3"	
28600 kHz	16' 4"	8' 2"	
28700 kHz	16' 4"	8' 2"	
28800 kHz	16' 3"	8' 2"	*10-meter amateur band*
28900 kHz	16' 2"	8' 1"	
29000 kHz	16' 2"	8' 1"	
29100 kHz	16' 1"	8'	
29200 kHz	16'	8'	
29300 kHz	15' 12"	7' 12"	
29400 kHz	15' 11"	7' 12"	
29500 kHz	15' 10"	7' 11"	
29600 kHz	15' 10"	7' 11"	
29700 kHz	15' 9"	7' 11"	
29800 kHz	15' 8"	7' 10"
29900 kHz	15' 8"	7' 10"
30000 kHz	15' 7"	7' 10"

B
APPENDIX

Resources

In addition to my own personal experiences with antenna design, construction, and installation, I received a great amount of information and helpful insights as a result of the work of others. Although not all of these resources made a direct impact on this book, they all provided an interesting background for it. These resources are included here as both a credit and for further reading.

Books

All About Aerials, Radio Publications, New York, NY, 1938.
The ARRL Antenna Book, American Radio Relay League, 1974.
Bennett, Hank; Hardy, David T.; Yoder, Andrew; *The Complete Shortwave Listener's Handbook (4th Edition)*, TAB Books, Blue Ridge Summit, PA, 1993.
Beverage and Longwire Antennas: Design and Theory, National Radio Club.
Carr, Joseph J., *Practical Antenna Handbook*, TAB Books, Blue Ridge Summit, PA, 1990.
Carr, Joseph J., *Practical Antenna Handbook (2nd Edition)*, TAB Books, Blue Ridge Summit, PA, 1994.
The Loop Antenna Book, National Radio Club.
McCormick, Anita L., *Shortwave Radio Listening for Beginners*, TAB Books, Blue Ridge Summit, PA, 1993.
The Radio Amateur's Handbook, American Radio Relay League, annual.
Traister, Robert J., *How To Build Hidden, Limited-Space Antennas That Work*, TAB Books, Blue Ridge Summit, PA, 1981.
Turner, Rufus P., *The Antenna Construction Handbook for Ham, CB & SWL*, TAB Books, Blue Ridge Summit, PA, 1978.

Magazines

Abraham, Lewis H., "Guys for Guys Who Have to Guy," *QST*, 6/55, p. 33–34, 142.
Alcorn, Earl M., "Folded Antenna for 160," *QST*, 12/41, p. 47–48.

Allen, S. M., "Condo Secret Agent," *73 Amateur Radio*, 5/83, p. 44–45.

"Antennas for 160 Meters," *QST*, 5/49, p. 27–29.

Arey, "Uncle Skip," "Static Crashes, Grocery Shopping and Ninja Antennas," *Monitoring Times*, 5/93, p. 40–41.

Arnold, James, "The Triangle Antenna," *QST,* 1/40, p. 20–21, 53.

Asson, Manfred, "A Simple Directive Antenna," *QST*, 2/37, p. 42, 110.

Atchley, Dana, "Putting the Quarter-Wave Sloper to Work on 160," *QST*, 7/79, p. 19–20.

Auld, Bruce, "The Easy PVC," *CQ*, 8/92, p. 20–24.

Auld, Bruce, "The Irrigator's Special," *CQ*, 4/92, p. 38–41.

Avery, John D., "Multi-Impedance Dipoles," *QST*, 5/53, p. 42–43.

Bacher, Rudolph J., "A Simple Fixed-Direction Quad," *QST*, 1/75, p. 23, 49.

Beers, Yardley, "Short Antennas for the Lower Frequencies," 9/70, p. 15–19.

Beers, Yardley, "An Unorthodox Antenna," *QST*, 3/36, p. 32–33.

Beers, Yardley, "The Wavelength Factor," *QST*, 2/52, p. 40–44, 116, 118.

Belrose, John S., "The Half Sloper—successful Deployment is an Enigma," *QST*, 5/80, p. 31–33.

Belrose, John S., "The HF Discone Antenna," *QST*, 7/75, p. 11–14, 56.

Belrose, John S., "A Kite-Supported 160- (or 80-) Meter Antenna," *QST*, 3/81, p. 40–42.

Belrose, J. S., "Short Antennas for Mobile Operation," *QST*, 9/53, p. 30–35, 108.

Belrose, John S., "Transmission-Line Low Profile Antennas," *QST*, 12/75, p. 19–25.

Bonebrake, Robert J., "Miniature Mobile Antenna," *QST*, 9/55, p. 33–35.

Boothe, Barry A., "The Minooka Special," *QST*, 12/74, p. 15–19, 28.

Botts, J. G., "A Four-Element Vertical Beam for 40/15 Meters," *QST*, 6/75, p. 30–33.

Braschwitz, Harold J., "Directional Antenna for the Transmitter Hunter," *QST*, 4/56, p. 30, 122.

Breuer, William J., "The 'Double Pitchfork' Antenna," *QST*, 7/39, p. 40–41.

Bridges, William, "The MABAV Mobile Antenna," *QST*, 8/70, p. 23–25.

Brown, Herrick B., "Electric Fence Wire for Antenna Use," *QST*, 11/54, p. 55.

Burhans, R. W., "Loop Antennas for VLF-LF," *Radio-Electronics*, 6/83, p. 83–87.

Burnham, Bruce, "A 15-Meter Beam for $10," *QST*, 11/80, p. 18–19.

Camillo, Charles C. and Purinton, Richard M., "A Broadband Antenna for 75 Meters," *QST*, 6/55, p. 11–13.

Carr, Joseph J., "Antennas & Things," *Popular Communications*, monthly column.

Carr, Joseph J., "Antenna Grounding Basics," *Modern Electronics*, 8/90, p. 66.

Carr, Joseph J., "Wire Antennas For Hams and SWL's," *Popular Electronics*, 8/91, p. 49–52.

Carr, Paul, "The N4PC Extended Lazy H Antenna," *CQ*, 4/92, p. 11–18.

Clasen, Bill, "The 'Simple Squirt' Beam," *QST*, 10/54, p. 20–21, 118.

Cooper, C. Drayton, "The Bi-square Array," *Ham Radio,* 5/90, p. 42–44.

Cope, R. L., "'All-Band' Antenna," *QST*, 12/54, p. 39.

Copeland, J. L., "Remote End-Fed Antenna with Coaxial Line," *QST*, 2/55, p. 24–25.

Corderman, R. C., "Lightning Protection for the Transmitting Antenna," *QST*, p. 36–37, 124, 126.

Countryman, G. L., "An Experimental All-Band Nondirectional Transmitting Antenna," *QST*, 6/49, p. 54–55.

Courtier-Dutton, David L., "Some Notes on a 7-MHz Linear-Loaded Quad," *QST*, p. 14–15, 40.

Cousins, George, "A DX Curtain for 15 Meters," *73 Amateur Radio Today*, 9/69, p. 4–6.

Czerwinski, W. Pete, "Budget 7-Mc. Vertical Antenna," *QST*, 11/55, p. 26–27.

Daily, Chuck, "A 15-Meter Beam 'On A Budget'," *QST*, 2/71, p. 41–43.

DeMaw, Doug, "Antenna Accessories For the Beginner," *QST*, 2/79, p. 15–19.

DeMaw, Doug, "Novi-Loop," *QST*, 10/73, p. 20–21, 32.

DeMaw, Doug, "Simple Gain Antennas for the Beginner," *QST*, 8/81, p. 32–35.

DeMaw, Doug, "Which Antenna to Use," *QST*, 5/81, p. 26–29.

Dezettel, L. M., "Measure Your Antenna Resonance," *Elementary Electronics*, p. 71–74.

Dougherty, J. J., "Re Ham Band Transmitting Loops," *QST*, 10/53, p. 52.

Eldred, Ellis, "Build a Coke-Bottle Antenna," *Electronics Handbook*, Fall 1987.

Ellingson, Gary L., "A Helically Wound Vertical Antenna for the 75-Meter Band," *QST*, 1/72, p. 32–33.

Elliot, Gary D., "Phased Verticals for 40," *QST*, 4/72, p. 18–20.

English, W. E., "A 40-Meter DDRR Antenna," *QST*, 12/71, p. 28–32.

Ferrier, D. T. and Baird, W. G., "A New Kind of Skyhook," *QST*, 10/46, p. 24–25.

Ferrill, T. M. Jr., "Simple Vertical Antennas," *QST*, 1/39, p. 47–49, 90, 92.

Ferrill, T. M. Jr., "Let's Settle Those Antennas Questions," *QST*, 11/38, p. 23–27.

Finger, Frank, "Lightning Protection," *73 Amateur Radio Today*, 7/91, p. 32.

Fleming, Norman L., "A Modified 20-Meter Delta-Loop Beam," *QST*, 6/73, p. 24–27.

Foskett, Gary L., "Putting Up Wire Antennas—The Easy Way," *QST*, 6/73, p. 58–59, 77.

Freedom, Tom C., "The Down-To-Earth 'Sky Hook'," *QST*, 4/71, p. 22–23.

Friedman, Herbert, "Antennas For the New Amateur," *Radio-TV Experimenter*, 12/64, p. 103–105 and *Elementary Electronics*, Spring 1965, p. 89–91.

Gardener, Corliss B., "A Sturdy 55-ft. Skyhook," *QST*, 10/47, p. 28.

Garretson, Thomas A., "New Antenna Mast Designs," *QST*, 5/44, p. 38–40.

Genaille, Richard A., "How To Build a Multi-Tap Unun," *CQ*, p. 28–32.

Getter, Carl M., "A Compact Two-Element Beam for Twenty," *QST*, 5/54, p. 25–26.

Gibilisco, Stan, "The Megaloop," *73 Amateur Radio Today*, 7/91, p. 29–30, 44.

Glover, Paul, "The Mono-Loop Delta Antenna," *QST*, 9/79, p. 33–36.

Goodman, Byron, "Fashions in Antennas," *QST*, 6/39, p. 14–18.

Graham, Robert C., "Long-Wire Directive Antennas," *QST*, 5/37, p. 42–46, 72, 74, 106.

Green Jr., James H., "Improving the Transmitting Loop," *QST*, 6/41, p. 24–26.

Greene, R. Carleton, "More on Balloon-Supported Antennas," *QST*, 11/40, p. 38–39, 82.

Griffin, Dana A., "Improving the Flying Skywire," *QST*, 4/40, p. 32–33, 106–110.

Gillo, Peter H., "A Practical 40-Meter Quad," *QST*, 5/73, p. 28–29.

Hall, Jerry, "Off-Center-Loaded Dipole Antennas," *QST*, 9/74, p. 28–24, 58.

Hall, Jerry, "Zip-Cord Antennas—Do They Work?" *QST*, 3/79, p. 31–32.

Hall, L. Scott, "A Discone Just For Fun," *73 Amateur Radio Today*, September 1993, p. 38–40.

Harbauch, Allen B., "Broad-Band 80-Meter Antenna," *QST*, 12/80, p. 36–37.

Hickman, Bob, "The Poly-Tower Phased Array," *QST*, 1/81, p. 30–34.

Haughton, Anson B., "An Unusual 75-Meter Mobile Antenna," *QST*, 1/54, p. 22.

Hood, W. Edmund, "Mobile Antenna Tips," *73 Amateur Radio*, 9/77, p. 160–163.

Hull, Ross A. and Rodimon, C. C., "Plain Talk about Rhombic Antennas," *QST*, 11/36, p. 28–29, 74, 100, 102, 106.

Hunt, James W., "Some Ideas for Low-Frequency Antennas," *QST*, 4/49, p. 28–29.

Jensen, L. J., "A Compact Dual Beam for 20 and 40 Meters," *QST*, 3/55, p. 11–13.

Keay, O. S. and Pehoushek, Joe, "A Cheap and Efficient Vertical Antenna for 7 and 14 Mc. Operation," *QST*, 10/36, p. 18–19, 72.

Keown, Malcolm P. and Lamb, Laimon L., "A Simple Technique for Tower Section Separation," *QST*, 9/79, p. 37–38.

Klagge, Neil, "A 160-Meter Short Dipole," *QST*, 10/70, p. 46.

Koester, Ronald B., "The W2EKY 'Icky-Stick' Antenna," *73 Amateur Radio Today*, September 1993, p. 18–19.

Kraus, John D., "Directional Antennas with Closely-Spaced Elements," *QST*, 1/38, p. 21–23, 37.

Kraus, John D., "W8JK 5-Band Rotary Beam Antenna," *QST*, 7/70, p. 11–14.

Lawson, James L., "A 75/80-Meter Vertical Square Array," *QST*, 3/71, p. 18–20.

Lawson, James L., "160/80/75-Meter Broad-Band Inverted-V Antenna," *QST*, 11/70, p. 17–20.

Lawson, James L., "Simple Arrays of Vertical Antenna Elements," *QST*, 5/71, p. 22–27.

Leinwoll, Stanley, "Shortwave Radio," *Radio-Electronics*, monthly column.

Leslie, S. B. Jr., "A Cubical Quad for 20 Meters," *QST*, 1/55, p. 21–23, 122.

Lewis, L. L., "A One-Man Skyhook," *QST*, 7/47, p. 19–20.

Ljongquist, E. W., "The Shooter—A 3-Band Portable Antenna," *QST*, 9/80, p. 23–25.

Lippman, Bill, "I Just Put Up A New Antenna," *QST*, 2/47, p. 66–68.

Longerich, Harry, "The CCD Antenna Revisited," *73 Amateur Radio Today*, 5/82, p. 40–41.

Lufkin, H. Warren, "The Powerful Grounded Antenna," *73 Amateur Radio*, 3/78, p. 26–27.

Lugar, Charles W., "A Rotary Spider-Web Loop Antenna With Reflector," *QST*, 12/37, p. 25–26, 90, 92, 94.

Lukoff, Herman, "An Accessible Antenna Tower," *QST*, 2/56, p. 22, 114, 116.

Lynch, Arthur, "Feeding Vertical Antennas," *QST*, 1/39, p. 13–17, 108, 110.

Marquart, W. E., "Calculations For Antenna Orientation," *QST*, 7/45, p. 46–47.

Marris, Richard Q., "Compressing the W3EDP," *73 Amateur Radio Today*, September 1993, p. 20–24.

McClelland, Jim, "Distributed Capacity Twisted Loop," *73 Amateur Radio Today*, September 1993, p. 26–27.

McCoy, Lewis G., "An 80- and 40-Meter Antenna System for the Novice," *QST*, 2/53, p. 29–31.

McCoy, Lewis G., "Let's Meet Mr. Ionosphere," *QST*, 8/54, p. 36–38, 112–116.

McCoy, Lew, "Let's Talk Antennas," *CQ*, 9-11/91.

McCoy, Lewis G., "A Low-Cost Tilt-Over Tower," *QST*, 11/71, p. 22–23.

McCoy, Lew, "Some Plain Facts about Multiband Vertical Antennas," *QST*, 9/72, p. 14–16.

McCoy, Lewis G., "Why A Beam Antenna?," *QST*, 1/72, p. 36–39.

Merry, Fred J., "A Switchable Multiband Ground-Plane Antenna," *QST*, 10/53, p. 44–45.

Millen, James, "A New Kind of Skyhook—The Ladder Mast," *QST*, 7/37, p. 16–18.

Mills, Harry A. and Brizendine, Gene, "Antenna Design: Something New," *73*, October 1978, p. 282–289.

Mix, Don, "Antennas for Domestic Work," *QST*, 9/41, p. 38–42, 94.

Moore, Morton E. and Johnson, F. L., "Directed Vertical Radiation with Diamond Antennas," *QST*, 4/37, p. 21–24, 51.

Moxon, L. A., "Two-Element Driven Arrays," *QST*, 7/52, p. 28–31, 120.

Meyers, Robert M. and Hall, Jerry, "Phased Verticals in a 40-Meter Beam-Switching Array," *QST*, p. 36–43.

Murphy, J. A., "Transmission Line Primer," *73 Amateur Radio*, 6/77, p. 124–126.

Nose, Katashi, "A 160-Meter Receiving Loop," *QST*, 4/75, p. 40–41.

Okleshen, Orlando O., "A Four-Band Whopper," *QST*, 4/74, p. 11–14.

Orloski, Ray, "Soldering to Aluminum," *QST*, 6/54, p. 42, 120.

Orr, H. T., "The Beer-Can Antenna, Minnesota Style," *QST*, 4/56, p. 23, 116.

Overbeck, Wayne E., "High Versus Low Antenna," *QST*, 3/70, p. 20–22.

Owen, Lawrence B., "The Vertical-V Antenna," *QST*, 5/81, p. 24–25.

Parrott, John H., "Quad vs. Triband Yagi," *QST*, 2/71, p. 11–13.

Penners, B., "A Directive Antenna for the Low Frequencies," *QST*, 2/44, p. 40–42.

Pool, John A., "A Three-Feeder Double-Antenna System," *QST*, 5/36, p. 49–50.

Potter, Mark L., "Establishing Antenna Resonance," *QST*, 5/48, p. 23–24.

Rappold, Sam, "Folded Unipole for 160," *73 Amateur Radio*, 10/81, p. 28–33.

Reinartz, John L. and Simpson, Burton T., "Concentrated Directional Antennas for Transmission and Reception," *QST*, 10/37, p. 27–30.

Rhodes, Peter D., "The Log-Periodic Dipole Array," *QST*, 11/73, p. 16–23.

Rhodes, Peter D., "The Log-Periodic V Array," *QST*, 10/79, p. 40–43.

Richartz, Willi, "A Stacked Multiband Vertical for 80–10 Meters," *QST*, 2/75, p. 44–45.

Roberts, Walter Van B., "Long-Wire Antennas," *QST*, 6/42, p. 36–39.

Rockey, C. F., "I.C.R.A." *Radio-TV Experimenter*, #562 1959, p. 158–159.

Romander, Hugo, "The Extended Double-Zepp Antenna," *QST*, 6/38, p. 12–16, 76–82.

Rowe, Norman L., "Let's Keep It Simple—Adjusting the Novice Antenna," *QST*, 9/53, p. 40–41.

Salmon, Walter E., "The 'Extended Lazy H' Antenna," *QST*, 10/55, p. 20.

Sandford, Wayne H. Jr., "A Modest 45-Foot DX Vertical for 160, 80, 40, and 30 Meters," *QST*, 9/81, p. 27–31.

Schellenbach, Richard R., "An Antenna For 7 Mc DX," *QST*, 6/47, p. 32.

Schultz, John J., "A New Look at Some Classic Wire Antennas," *CQ*, 1/91, p. 32–34.

Schultz, Walter J., "The Göttingen Heart Antenna," *Ham Radio*, 5/90, p. 11–17.

Scotten, A. F., "The Invisible Antenna," *QST*, 2/49, p. 46–47.

Sevick, Jerry, "The Ground-Image Vertical Antenna," *QST*, 7/71, p. 16–19, 22.

Sevick, Jerry, "The W2FMI Ground-Mounted Short Vertical," *QST*, 3/73, p. 13–18, 41.

Shaver, Daniel P., "Dirt Cheap Directional Array," *73 Amateur Radio*, 8/77, p. 40–41.

Silberstein, Richard, "Some Simple Ways of Erecting Temporary and Semi-Permanent Antennas," *QST*, 3/52, p. 40–41, 114, 116.

Skitzki, Paul, "The QH (Quick Heading) Beam Antenna," *QST*, 6/52, p. 50–52.

Stavrou, Nick C., "Simple Directional Arrays Using Half-Wave Elements," *QST*, 5/38, p. 17–19, 108, 110.

Stiles, Ed, "How to Wind a Hassle-Free HF Helix," *CQ*, 8/92, p. 52.

Stiles, Walter J., "Dual-Polarization DX Antennas," *QST*, 3/72, p. 22–23, 43.

Swafford, Thomas W., "The Twin-Loop Antenna," *QST*, 3/52, p. 24–25.

Swift, L. M., "A 'Double-Barrelled' Antenna System," *QST*, 4/39, p. 22–23, 102.

Taylor, L. L., "Vertical Multiband Antenna," *QST*, 5/55, p. 19–21.

Thurber, Karl T., "Antennas & Accessories," *CQ*, monthly column.

Trauffer, Arthur, "Aluminum Folding Rule Antenna," *Radio-TV Experimenter*, 1952 #2, p. 107.

Trowbridge, Byron, "A DeLuxe Rotary Antenna Structure," *QST*, p. 26–29, 100–102.

Turner, James A., "Verti-Beam III—A Multidirection 20-Meter Antenna," *QST*, 8/80, p. 26–27.

Turrin, Dick, "Antenna Performance Measurements," *QST*, 11/74, p. 35–41.

Tyskewicz, John, "The Heli-Rope Antenna," *QST*, 6/71, p. 32–33.

Van Zant, F. N., "160, 75, and 40 Meter Inverted Dipole Loop," *QST*, 1/73, p. 37–39.

Vincent, W. R., "A Closer Look at the HF Resonant Dipole," *QST*, 10/72, p. 48–49, 55.

Vissers, William, "High Q Antennas," *73 Amateur Radio*, 9/78, p. 68–71.

Wallace, Don C., "Making the Most of Directive Antennas," *QST*, 11/37, p. 35–37, 106–108.

Ward, Allen C., "A Simple Multiband HF Vertical Antenna," *73 Amateur Radio*, 4/90, p. 89–90.

Webster, Robert E., "Mobile Loop Antennas," *QST*, 6/54, p. 26–27.

Wilson, Robert; "Nonresonant Delta and V Beam Antennas," *Ham Radio*, 5/90, p. 49–52.

Wintzer, Mike, "Dipole Passe," *QST*, 10/74, p. 15–18, 21.

Wolfert, Lawrence, "The Tower Alternative," *QST*, 11/80, p. 36–37.

Woodward, R. W., "More About Soldering Aluminum," *QST*, 9/54, p. 39.

Wrigley, William B., "Folded and Loaded Antennas," *QST*, 4/53, p. 21–27, 128.

Wrigley, William B., "Impedance Characteristics of Harmonic Antennas," *QST*, 2/54, p. 10–14, 100.

C
APPENDIX

Suppliers

This section contains the names, addresses, and telephone numbers for several suppliers of electronics parts, antenna wire, coaxial cable, connectors, shortwave radios, and tools for completing antennas. Some of these sources also have commercially constructed antennas.

At this writing, these addresses and phone numbers are correct. However, companies and locations change from time to time, so a few of these listings might be obsolete by the time you read this.

Accord Electronics
1001 NW 62nd SE #306F
Ft. Lauderdale, FL 33309
(800) 998-2242

Alltronics
2300 Zanker Rd.
San Jose, CA 95131
(408) 943-9773

Alpha Delta Communications
P.O. Box 51117
Phoenix, AZ 85076

American Electronics
164 Southpark Blvd.
P.O.Box 301
Greenwood, IN 46142
(800) 872-1373

American Radio Relay League
225 Main St.
Newington CT, 06111

Antenna Supermarket
P.O. Box 563
Palantine, IL 60078

Antennas West
1500 N. 150 West
Provo, UT 84605

Arrow Electronics Corp.
25 Hub Dr.
Melville, NY 11747

Barry Electronics Corp.
512 Broadway
New York City, NY 10012
(212) 925-7000

Brigar Electronics
7-9 Alice St.
Binghamton, NY 13094
(607) 723-3111

C&H Sales
2176 E. Colorado Blvd.
Pasadena, CA 91107

Communications Electronics
P.O. Box 1045
Ann Arbor, MI 48106
(313) 996-8888

Crump Electronics
6340 W. Mississippi Ave.
Lakewood, CO 80226
(303) 936-4407

Digi-Key
Box 677
Thief River Falls, MN 56701

Digitronics Surplus
P.O. Box 933
Olalla, WA 98359

Electronic Equipment Bank
323 Mill St. NE
Vienna, VA 22180
(800) 368-3270

Electronics Goldmine
Box 5408
Scottsdale, AZ 85261
(602) 451-7454

Fair Radio Sales
P.O. Box 1105
Lima, OH 45802
(419) 227-6573

Gateway Electronics
8123 Page Blvd.
St. Louis, MO 63130
(314) 427-6116

Gilfer Shortwave
52 Park Ave.
Park Ridge, NJ 07656

Global Connections
P.O. Box 173
Middleport, NY 14105
(716) 315-9418

Grove Enterprises
140 Dog Branch Rd.
P.O. Box 98
Brasstown, NC 28902
(800) 438-8155

Hosefelt Electronics
2700 Sunset Blvd.
Steubenville, OH 43952
(800) 524-6464

IME
P.O. Box 170415
Arlington, TX 76003

Keystone Electronics
31-07 20th Rd.
Astoria, NY 11105
(718) 956-8900

JAMECO
1355 Shoreway Rd.
Belmont, CA 94002
(800) 831-4242

Javanco
501 12th Ave. South
Nashville, TN 37203
(615) 244-4444

Johnson Shop Products
Box 160113
Cupertino, CA 95016
(408) 257-8614

Jones, Marlin P.
P.O. Box 12685
Lake Park, FL 33403
(407) 848-8236

Kelvin Electronics
7 Fairchild Ave.
Plainview, NY 11803
(516) 349-7620

Liolaemus Designs
Box 360866
Milpitas, CA 95036
(408) 263-8944

MCM Electronics
650 Congress Park Dr.
Centerville, OH 45459

Mendelson Electronics Co.
3340 1st St.
Dayton, OH 45402
(800) 344-4465

Marymac
22511 Katy Fwy.
Katy, TX 77450
(713) 392-0747

MFJ Enterprises
P.O. Box 494
Mississippi State, MS 39762
(800) 647-1800

Mil-Spec Communications
P.O. Box 461
Wakefield, RI 02880
(401) 783-7106

Mouser Electronics
2401 Hwy. 287N
Mansfield, TX 76063
(800) 346-6873

Newark Electronics
4801 N. Ravenswood Ave.
Chicago, IL 60640

Ocean State Electronics
P.O. Box 1458
Westerly, RI 02891
(800) 866-6626

Pak Rat Electronics
P.O. Box 690073
Houston, TX 77269
(713) 893-0313

Palomar Enterprises
P.O. Box 462222
Escondido, CA 92046
(619) 747-3343

Parts Express
340 E. 1st St.
Dayton, OH 45402
(513) 222-0173

Prime Components
33 Freeman St.
Newark, NJ 07105
(201) 344-1029

PS Technology Inc.
714 Warren Rd.
Cockeysville, MD 21030
(410) 667-4889

RA Enterprises
2260 DeLa Cruz Blvd.
Santa Clara, CA 95050
(408) 986-8286

Southpaw Electronics
P.O. Box 886
New Hyde Park, NY 11040

Surplus Sales of Nebraska
1315 Jones St.
Omaha, NE 68102
(402) 346-4750

Tucker Electronics
P.O. Box 551419
Dallas, TX 75335
(800) 527-4642

Universal Radio
6830 American Pkwy.
Reynoldsburg, OH 43068
(800) 431-3939

Glossary

angle of radiation The angle, relative to the horizon, at which a radio signal departs from an antenna.

antenna Any object used to pick up radio signals. Most antennas are cut to a length that is resonant at the frequency at which it is intended to be used.

antenna tuner A piece of equipment that matches the impedance the receiver or transmitter to the feedline for maximum signal transfer.

armstrong rotator An archaic hand-crank method of turning an antenna or antenna mast.

balun A balanced/unbalanced device that adapts a balanced antenna to an unbalanced transmission line.

beam antenna Any antenna that features reflector or director elements.

beverage antenna A terminated longwire antenna situated very low to the ground across its entire length.

boom The material on which the driven, reflector, and director elements of a beam antenna are fixed.

coaxial cable A type of cable primarily used to transport a radio signal from the antenna to the receiver. Standard coaxial cable consists of an inner wire, an insulating dielectric, a shielding braid, and an outside insulating jacket.

cold solder joint A solder joint that is neither electrically nor mechanically solid.

counterpoise A system to electrically ground an antenna without actually having a physical connection to earth.

cubical quad A type of loop antenna in which a box-shaped driven element is used in conjunction with similar box-shaped reflectors and/or directors.

delta loop A triangular-shaped loop antenna.

dipole A balanced half-wave antenna consisting of two horizontal quarter-wave elements.

director Used in beam antennas; an antenna element not electrically connected to the transmission line yet mounted in front of it to direct signals to the driven element.

driven element Used in beam antennas; the antenna element that is electrically connected to the transmission line.

egg insulator An egg-shaped insulator used to insulate the end of a wire antenna from the ropes that hold the antenna in the air; sometimes called an **end insulator**.

ground plane A type of counterpoise that usually consists of quarter-wave wires or tubes that radiate from the bottom of a vertical antenna.

ground wave The part of a radio signal that radiates at a level parallel to the ground.

guy wires Wires or ropes used to support a tower or mast.

impedance The opposition of a component to alternating current.

interference Any signal that damages the reception of the radio station you are listening to.

inverted V A form of dipole antenna in which the center is the highest point and the two ends point toward the ground.

ionosphere A layer of the atmosphere in which molecules are charged by solar radiation. Radio signals are refracted or absorbed by the ionosphere.

insulator A nonconductive element used to isolate different antenna parts from each other or from the environment. The most common types for hobbyists are glass, ceramic, or plastic egg or center insulators.

lightning arrestor A small circuit that normally allows signals to travel between the antenna and the radio but directs large signals, such as lightning blasts, toward the ground to protect the electronic equipment.

loading coil A coil used to effectively electrically shorten an antenna.

longwire An end-fed antenna that consists of a single piece of wire that is over 100' long.

loop antenna A directional antenna that consists of one or more loops of wire or tubing.

mast A wooden, PVC, or metal vertical length used to support the center or ends of an antenna.

parasitic elements A general name for the reflector and director elements of a beam antenna.

propagation The transfer of radio signals from the transmitting antenna to the receiving antenna.

quarter-wave vertical An antenna that consists of a vertical quarter-wavelength piece of wire or tubing and a standard, counterpoise, or ground-plane ground.

radials One of the two major types of ground systems. Quarter-wavelength wires are soldered at a central point and radiate out from that point.

radiator In transmitting, the part of an antenna that radiates the signal.

reflector Used in beam antennas; an antenna element not electrically connected to the transmission line yet mounted behind it to reflect signals to the driven element.

resonance The point at which the antenna is the same length as or a harmonic of the frequency in question.

rhombic A diamond-shaped end-fed antenna that exhibits a very directional transmitting and receiving pattern.

skip The phenomenon that occurs when a radio signal bounces off the earth, is refracted by the atmosphere, and is received at another location.

sky wave Any radio signal that has been refracted back to earth via the ionosphere.

sloper A form of dipole antenna in which one end is mounted high above the ground and the other near the ground so that the antenna slopes toward the ground.

transmission line One of various types of wires or cabling that transports radio signals from an antenna to a receiver or from a transmitter to an antenna.

twin-lead A type of transmission line that consists of two parallel wires embedded in plastic insulation.

wavelength The length, directly related to the frequency, of each radio wave. Shortwave wavelengths vary from approximately 615' (1600 kHz) to approximately 33' (30 MHz).

yagi antenna A highly directional antenna containing parallel antenna elements that reflect and direct the incoming signals to the driven element.

Index

About the Author

At the tender age of 13, Andrew Yoder became addicted to shortwave listening on a World War II era Hallicrafters SX-28A in the basement of one of his best friends. Since that time, he has spent numerous hours glued to radios, in search of shortwave and pirate broadcast stations. Andrew has been bitten by the nostalgia bug and currently owns a small lineup of tube radios from the 1940s through the 1960s. His articles have appeared in *Popular Communications*, *Popular Electronics*, and *New Jersey Monthly*, and he writes regular columns for several newsletters in North America and Europe. His recent books include *Pirate Radio Stations: Tuning into Underground Broadcasts (2nd Edition)* and *The Complete Shortwave Listener's Handbook (4th Edition)*.